A-Level Year 1 & AS
Chemistry
Exam Board: OCR A

Let's face it — AS Chemistry exams are no picnic. If you want to do well, you'll really need to know your stereoisomers from your successive ionisation energies.

Happily, this fantastic Exam Practice Workbook from CGP will help make sure you're 100% ready for the real thing. It's packed with exam-style questions for the whole AS course (and Year 1 of A-Level), with full answers and mark schemes included.

We've even thrown in some expert tips to help you pick up maximum marks, so the final exams should seem a lot less daunting when the big day rolls around.

CGP

A-Level revision? It has to be CGP!

Published by CGP

Editors:
Alex Billings, Katie Burton, Mary Falkner, Paul Jordin, Caroline Purvis, Emily Sheraton.

Contributors:
Sarah Binns, Mike Dagless, David Paterson, Megan Pollard, Andy Rankin, Sarah Rich, Louise Watkins.

IR spectrum on page 66 — Source: NIST Chemistry WebBook (http://webbook.nist.gov/chemistry).
IR spectrum on page 70 — Adapted from NIST Chemistry WebBook (http://webbook.nist.gov/chemistry).
Mass spectrum on page 69 — Adapted from NIST Chemistry WebBook (http://webbook.nist.gov/chemistry).

ISBN: 978 1 78294 920 6

With thanks to Barrie Crowther and Glenn Rogers for the proofreading.

With thanks to Ana Pungartnik for the copyright research.

Printed by Elanders Ltd, Newcastle upon Tyne

Based on the classic CGP style created by Richard Parsons.

Illustrations by: Sandy Gardner Artist, email sandy@sandygardner.co.uk

Contents

Use the tick boxes to check off the topics you've completed.

Module 1 (Development of Practical Skills) is tested in context throughout this book, alongside Modules 2 to 4.

Exam Advice..2

Module 2 — Foundations in Chemistry

Atoms, Compounds and Equations ....3 ☐

Amount of Substance, Acids and Redox ....7 ☐

Electrons, Bonding and Structure ....20 ☐

Module 3 — Periodic Table and Energy

The Periodic Table ....28 ☐

Physical Chemistry ....38 ☐

Module 4 — Core Organic Chemistry

Basic Concepts and Hydrocarbons ....50 ☐

Alcohols, Haloalkanes and Analysis ....61 ☐

Mixed Questions

Mixed Questions ....71 ☐

Answers 78

Data Sheet 97

Exam Advice

To pick up every mark you can, you'll need tip-top exam technique as well as your knowledge of chemistry.

Get Familiar with the **Exam Structure**

If you're sitting A-level Chemistry rather than AS, you'll be sitting a different set of exams to the ones described here. The exams will include the same types of questions though.

For **AS Chemistry**, you'll be sitting **two papers**.

Breadth in chemistry (Modules 1 to 4) **1 hour 30 minutes**　　70 marks　　**50%** of your AS	**20 marks** of **multiple choice** questions. **50 marks** of **short** answer questions and **extended response** questions.
Depth in chemistry (Modules 1 to 4) **1 hour 30 minutes**　　70 marks　　**50%** of your AS	**Short answer** and **extended response** questions.

1) As you can see, **both papers** test you on **Modules 1 to 4**. Module 1 relates to **practical skills**. The Module 1 theory is tested in context throughout this book, alongside Modules 2 to 4.

2) Your **maths skills** will also be tested in both papers.

3) **Short answer** questions could include **structured** questions, **calculations** and **problem solving**.

4) In the 'Depth in chemistry' exam some of the **extended response** questions will be marked using a '**Level of Response**' mark scheme. For these questions, you'll be marked based on the **quality** of your responses as well as their chemistry **content**. Your answers will need to be **coherent** and **fully explained**, and have a **logical structure**. Questions marked using a 'Level of Response' mark scheme will be shown with an **asterisk** (*) next to their number.

Manage Your Time Sensibly

1) Use the **number of marks** available to help you decide **how long** to spend on a question.

2) Some questions will require **lots of work** for only a **few** marks but others may be much quicker. **Don't** spend ages struggling with questions that are only worth a couple of marks — move on. You can always **come back** to them later when you've bagged loads of marks elsewhere.

3) **Multiple choice** questions can sometimes be quite **time-consuming**, but they're still only worth **one mark** each. So if you're pressed for time, you might want to focus on the **written answer** questions, where there are **more marks** available.

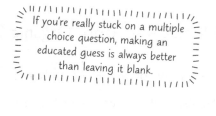
If you're really stuck on a multiple choice question, making an educated guess is always better than leaving it blank.

Be Careful Drawing **Diagrams**

1) Draw all your diagrams nice and big, so you can clearly show all the **detail** you need to get the marks.

2) Make sure you include **everything** the question **asks** for in your answer.

3) When you're drawing **mechanisms**, remember to pay close attention to your **curly arrows**. They need to be clearly coming from a **lone pair**, **negative charge** or **bond** for you to get the marks.

4) If you're asked to draw a particular type of **formula**, make sure you give your answer in the format asked for. For example, if you're asked for a **displayed** formula **don't** draw a **skeletal** formula instead.

Remember to Use the **Exam Data Sheet**

1) In your exams, you'll be given a **data sheet**. It'll contain lots of **useful information**, such as:
   - the characteristic **infrared absorptions** of some bonds in organic molecules,
   - some **constants** and **conversions**,
   - a copy of the **periodic table**.

2) You'll find a **data sheet** containing the above information on **pages 97** and **98** of this book.

Atoms, Compounds and Equations

Got to start somewhere, so how about a nice recap of basic atomic structure, relative masses and ionic formulae? Of course it's not all *quite* that simple, there are a couple of tricky equations to balance, but overall it's not too bad.

For each of questions 1-4, give your answer by writing the correct letter in the box.

1 How many neutrons would you find in the nucleus of a copper-64 atom?

A   29   B   34

C   35   D   64

Your answer ☐

(1 mark)

2 What is the formula of caesium selenide?

A Cs_2Se B $CsSe$

C $CsSe_2$ D $CsSe_4$

Your answer ☐

(1 mark)

3 Which row shows the atomic structure of $^{109}Ag^+$?

	Protons	Neutrons	Electrons
A	47	62	47
B	47	62	46
C	46	63	47
D	47	60	46

Your answer ☐

(1 mark)

4 A sample of neon has a relative atomic mass of 20.187. The relative abundances of all the isotopes present in the sample are given in the table below. Which isotope of neon is isotope **X**?

Isotope	Neon-21	Neon-20	X
Relative abundance / %	0.3	90.5	9.2

A   Neon-19   B   Neon-22

C   Neon-24   D   Neon-23

Your answer ☐

(1 mark)

4

5   The diagram below shows an isotope of oxygen.

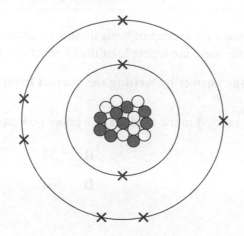

(a) (i)   State the meaning of the term isotopes.

....

....

(1 mark)

(ii) Give the mass number and the atomic number of the isotope shown.

mass number: ....   atomic number: ....

(1 mark)

(b) Oxygen typically forms ions with a 2– charge. Give the number of electrons in an O^{2-} ion.

....

(1 mark)

(c) The diagram is based on a model of the atom that is widely used today.
     Suggest why this model is still used by scientists when more accurate models have since been developed.

....

....

....

(2 marks)

6   Copper(II) sulfate solution reacts with aqueous sodium hydroxide to form a precipitate
of copper(II) hydroxide.

(a) (i)   Give the formula of the soluble salt also produced in the reaction.

....

(1 mark)

(ii) Write the simplest ionic equation for the reaction occurring. Include state symbols.

....

....

(1 mark)

(b) (i)   Sodium hydroxide also reacts with sulfuric acid to form a salt and water.
           Write a balanced symbol equation for this reaction.

....

(1 mark)

(ii) By considering the ions reacting and the species being formed, show that your equation in **(b) (i)** can be simplified to the ionic equation for neutralisation ($H^+ + OH^- \rightarrow H_2O$).

....

....

(2 marks)

7 Mass spectrometry is a technique used by scientists to help identify elements and compounds.

The mass spectrum of a sample of an element, **J**, is shown below.

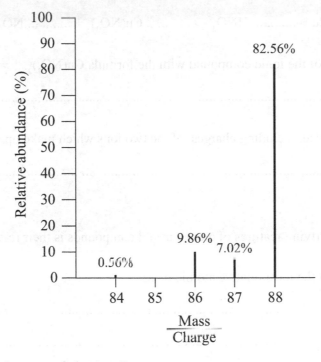

(a) Calculate the relative atomic mass of element **J**.
Give your answer to **one** decimal place.

A_r of element **J** = ...

(2 marks)

(b) Use your answer to **(a)** and the Periodic Table to identify element **J**.

....

(1 mark)

8 Nitric oxide, NO, is a colourless gas at room temperature and pressure.

(a) Nitric oxide reacts with carbon monoxide, CO, to give nitrogen and one other gaseous product.
Suggest a balanced symbol equation for this reaction.

....

(2 marks)

(b) Nitric oxide reacts with propanone to produce CH_3COOCH_3.
Give the relative molecular mass of CH_3COOCH_3.

M_r = ...

(1 mark)

(c) (i) Nitric oxide is produced in the oxidation of ammonia and the reaction of copper with dilute nitric acid. Unbalanced equations for these reactions are shown below. Balance these equations.

$$\ldots\ldots\ NH_3 + \ldots\ldots\ O_2 \rightarrow \ldots\ldots\ NO + \ldots\ldots\ H_2O$$

$$3Cu + \ldots\ldots\ HNO_3 \rightarrow \ldots\ldots\ Cu(NO_3)_2 + \ldots\ldots\ NO + \ldots\ldots\ H_2O$$

(2 marks)

(ii) Give the name of the ionic compound with the formula $Cu(NO_3)_2$.

....

(1 mark)

(iii) State the formulae, including charges, of the two ions which make up $Cu(NO_3)_2$.

....

(1 mark)

9 One of the key identifying features of elements and compounds is their relative mass.

(a) State the meaning of the term relative atomic mass.

....

....

(2 marks)

(b) Describe how relative isotopic mass differs from relative atomic mass.

....

....

(1 mark)

(c) Calculate the M_r of the copper-containing complex $[Cu(NH_3)_4(H_2O)_2]^{2+}$.

M_r = ...

(1 mark)

(d) Potassium manganate(VII), $KMnO_4$, reacts with hydrochloric acid to produce three chlorine-containing species. Two of these species have M_r values of 71.0 and 125.9. Suggest the formulae of these two species.

.... and ....

(2 marks)

EXAM TIP

If you're finding balancing equations, tricky, you could try jotting down how many of each type of atom you've got on each side of the equation to begin with. Then start trying some numbers in the equation (in pencil at first), and update the number of atoms on each side. Keep going until the numbers of atoms on both sides match. Then you can fill in your final answer in pen.

Score

30

Amount of Substance, Acids and Redox — 1

Maths skills are super-important in chemistry, and this section's crammed with questions to help you practise using them. There's a bit on acid-base reactions and redox reactions too, to keep things exciting

For each of questions 1-4, give your answer by writing the correct letter in the box.

1   How many chlorine atoms are present in one mole of PCl_5?

    A 6.02×10^{23}

    B 3.01×10^{24}

    C 6.02×10^{24}

    D 3.01×10^{23}

Your answer ☐

Remember, you can find any constants you need on the data sheet on pages 97-98.

(1 mark)

2   Vanadyl sulfate has the chemical formula $VOSO_4$.
What is the oxidation number of vanadium in vanadyl sulfate?

    A   +2   **B**   +3

    C   +4   **D**   +6

Your answer ☐

(1 mark)

3   A scientist burned 1.86 g of phosphorus in oxygen. 4.26 g of an oxide of phosphorus was produced. What is the empirical formula of this oxide?

    A PO_2 **B** P_2O_4

    C P_2O_5 **D** P_4O_{10}

Your answer ☐

(1 mark)

4   Excess barium chloride solution can react with copper sulfate solution to form a precipitate of barium sulfate: $BaCl_{2(aq)} + CuSO_{4(aq)} \rightarrow CuCl_{2(aq)} + BaSO_{4(s)}$

What volume of 0.650 mol dm^{-3} copper sulfate solution is needed to form 3.16 g of barium sulfate ($M_r = 233.4$)?

    A   87.8 cm^3

    B   0.0208 cm^3

    C   20.8 cm^3

    D   8.80 cm^3

Your answer ☐

(1 mark)

Module 2 — Foundations in Chemistry

5 Ascorbic acid is more commonly known as vitamin C. It has the following composition by mass: 40.9% carbon, 4.5% hydrogen and 54.6% oxygen.

(a) Determine the empirical formula of ascorbic acid.

empirical formula = ...
(2 marks)

(b) The relative molecular mass (M_r) of ascorbic acid is 176.0.
Determine the molecular formula of ascorbic acid.

molecular formula = ...
(1 mark)

(c) A vitamin C tablet contains 300 mg of ascorbic acid.
Calculate the number of moles of ascorbic acid in one tablet.

number of moles = ...
(1 mark)

6 Limewater is an aqueous solution of calcium hydroxide.

Calcium hydroxide solution reacts with dilute hydrochloric acid according to the equation:

$$2HCl_{(aq)} + Ca(OH)_{2(aq)} \rightarrow CaCl_{2(aq)} + 2H_2O_{(l)}$$

A student has a 25.0 cm³ sample of limewater of unknown concentration. She adds the sample to a volumetric flask and makes it up to 250 cm³ with distilled water. She then carries out a titration to determine the volume of 0.100 mol dm⁻³ hydrochloric acid needed to neutralise 25.0 cm³ of the diluted limewater solution.

(a) State the dependent variable in this experiment.

....
(1 mark)

The student's results are shown in the table below.

		Titre		
	Rough	1	2	3
Initial reading / cm³	11.10	28.50	11.25	27.60
Final reading / cm³	28.50	45.15	27.60	44.30
Volume of HCl added / cm³				

(b) (i) Complete the table by filling in the volume of hydrochloric acid added for each titre.
(2 marks)

(ii) Calculate the mean titre using the results shown in the table.

mean titre = ... cm³

(2 marks)

(iii) Determine the concentration of calcium hydroxide in mol dm⁻³ in the original limewater sample. Give your answer to an appropriate number of significant figures.

concentration = ... mol dm⁻³

(4 marks)

7   Butane gas (C_4H_{10}, M_r = 58.0) is used in camping stoves. A cylinder of volume 750 cm³ contains 2.30 g of the butane gas.

Remember, any constants you might need are on the data sheet on pages 97-98.

(a) Calculate the pressure, in kPa, exerted by the gas on the inside of the container at a temperature of 10.0 °C. Give your answer to an appropriate number of significant figures.

pressure = ... kPa

(4 marks)

Butane burns in oxygen to produce carbon dioxide and water: $C_4H_{10} + 6.5O_2 \rightarrow 4CO_2 + 5H_2O$

(b) Calculate the mass of butane burned during complete combustion with 3.84 g of oxygen gas.

mass = ... g

(3 marks)

EXAM TIP

If a question asks you to give your answer to an appropriate number of significant figures, it just means you need to round your final answer to the lowest number of significant figures that's in the data you're given. You'll get a whole mark just for doing that. Don't be tempted to round too soon though — always use the full, unrounded answers from any intermediate calculations.

Score

24

Amount of Substance, Acids and Redox — 2

1 A student is preparing 250 cm³ of a standard solution of sodium hydrogencarbonate ($NaHCO_3$).

She uses the following method:

1. Weigh out the required mass of sodium hydrogencarbonate into a weighing boat.
2. Tip the solid into a 250 cm³ volumetric flask.
3. Add distilled water to the flask until the bottom of the meniscus touches the line.
4. Stopper the flask and turn it upside down a few times to mix the contents.

(a) State **two** ways in which the student's method could be improved.

1. ....

....

2. ....

....

(2 marks)

The student fixes the mistakes in her method and repeats the procedure.
She makes a standard solution with a concentration of 0.30 mol dm⁻³.

(b) (i) Calculate the mass of sodium hydrogencarbonate that would be required to make a 250 cm³ solution with a concentration of 0.30 mol dm⁻³.

mass = ... g

(2 marks)

(ii) The student pours 100 cm³ of the solution into a beaker containing 150 cm³ of distilled water. Calculate the concentration of the solution in the beaker in mol dm⁻³.

concentration = ... mol dm⁻³

(2 marks)

The student then carries out a titration of a standard solution of sodium hydroxide against 25 cm³ of hydrochloric acid. She adds the hydrochloric acid and indicator to a conical flask. The standard solution of sodium hydroxide is then slowly added from a burette.

The student makes the following errors when preparing the standard solution of sodium hydroxide:

1. She didn't notice that the mass balance was showing a negative reading before the solid sodium hydroxide was weighed out.
2. Some of the sodium hydroxide was spilt on the bench when the student transferred it from the weighing boat to the volumetric flask.

(c) State and explain how each of these errors would affect the mean titre volume.

....

....

....

(2 marks)

2 Metals can be extracted from their ores using chemical reactions.

(a) Galena (PbS) is a common ore of lead. The extraction of lead from galena is a two-step process.

Step 1: $2PbS + 3O_2 \rightarrow 2PbO + 2SO_2$ **Step 2:** $2PbO + C \rightarrow 2Pb + CO_2$

(i) Calculate the mass of oxygen needed to react with 4.50 tonnes of PbS in **Step 1**.
(1 tonne = 1000 kg)

mass = ... kg
(3 marks)

(ii) Calculate the mass of lead that can be produced from 4.50 tonnes of PbS.

mass = ... kg
(2 marks)

(b) The Kroll process is used to extract titanium from its ore. The final step in the Kroll process involves the reaction of titanium(IV) chloride, $TiCl_4$, with a more reactive metal, usually magnesium or sodium.

Calculate the atom economies of reactions A and B shown below.

Reaction A: $TiCl_4 + 2Mg \rightarrow Ti + 2MgCl_2$ **Reaction B:** $TiCl_4 + 4Na \rightarrow Ti + 4NaCl$

atom economy of **reaction A** = ... %

atom economy of **reaction B** = ... %
(2 marks)

Other important metal ores include pyrolusite and hematite.

(c) (i) The chemical name for pyrolusite is manganese(IV) oxide.
Write the formula of manganese(IV) oxide.

....
(1 mark)

(ii) Hematite has the formula Fe_2O_3. Give the chemical name of hematite.

....
(1 mark)

12

3   This question is about the reactions of copper and copper compounds.

(a)   When copper metal reacts with cold, dilute nitric acid, Cu^{2+} ions and NO form according to the equation:

$$2HNO_3 + 3Cu + 6H^+ \rightarrow 3Cu^{2+} + 2NO + 4H_2O$$

     (i)   Explain, with reference to oxidation numbers, why this is a redox reaction.

           ....

           ....

           ....

           ....

           (4 marks)

     (ii)   Explain in terms of electron transfer what happens when a species is reduced

           ....

           (1 mark)

(b)   Copper metal may be extracted from sulfide ores by reaction with oxygen.
      The overall equation for the reduction of copper(I) sulfide, Cu_2S, to copper by oxygen is:

$$Cu_2S + O_2 \rightarrow 2Cu + SO_2$$

     (i)   A sample of Cu_2S reacts to form 3.60 g of Cu. The percentage yield for this reaction is 92.4%.
          Calculate the mass of the Cu_2S sample.
          Give your answer to an appropriate number of significant figures.

          mass = ... g

          (4 marks)

     (ii)   Determine the atom economy of this reaction.

          atom economy = ... %

          (1 mark)

     (iii)   Give **two** benefits for sustainability of choosing reactions with high atom
          economies over reactions with low atom economies for use in industry.

           ....

           ....

           ....

           (2 marks)

4 Ammonia is produced in the Haber Process.

Any constants you might need are on the data sheet on pages 97-98.

(a) (i) 0.0820 moles of ammonia gas was trapped in a gas jar at a temperature of 298 K and pressure of 101 kPa. Use the ideal gas equation to calculate the volume of the gas jar used to trap the ammonia.

volume = ... dm³

(3 marks)

(ii) Calculate the number of ammonia molecules in this sample.

....

(1 mark)

(b) Gaseous ammonia can react with water to form ammonium hydroxide.
A scientist is analysing a sample of ammonium hydroxide which contains
40.0% nitrogen and 14.3% hydrogen by mass. The rest of the mass is oxygen.

Use this data to show that the empirical formula of ammonium hydroxide is NH_5O.

(3 marks)

(c) A scientist bubbles gaseous ammonia through water, producing an alkaline solution.

(i) Write an equation to show how ammonia reacts with water to produce an alkaline solution.

....

(1 mark)

The scientist then neutralises this solution using nitric acid.

(ii) Write the formula of the salt formed in this neutralisation reaction.

....

(1 mark)

The good news is you'll be given the values of any constants you need in your exam on the data sheet. The bad news is you still need to know all the formulae and equations for calculations (e.g. mole calculations and atom economy) off by heart. Formula triangles can help, but the best way to make them stick is generally just to get plenty of practice using them.

Score

38

Amount of Substance, Acids and Redox — 3

1   HClO is a weak acid commonly known as hypochlorous acid.

(a)   Write an equation for the dissociation of HClO in solution.

....

(1 mark)

(b)   Deduce the oxidation number of Cl in HClO.

....

(1 mark)

(c)   HClO reacts with the alkali NaOH in an acid-base reaction.

$$HClO_{(aq)} + NaOH_{(aq)} \rightarrow NaClO_{(aq)} + H_2O_{(l)}$$

(i)   Explain what is meant by the term alkali.

....

....

(2 marks)

(ii)   Give the full chemical name of NaClO, using a Roman numeral to indicate the oxidation number.

....

(1 mark)

(iii) Write the simplest ionic equation for this reaction. Include state symbols.

....

(1 mark)

2   Hydrated barium chloride crystals have the formula $BaCl_2.nH_2O$. A student carried out an experiment to find the value of n in the formula. They used a 2 decimal place balance to measure the mass of an empty crucible, then placed a sample of the crystals in the crucible and measured the mass again. They heated the sample for 5 minutes, then measured the mass of the crucible and crystals once more.

The table below shows the results of the student's experiment.

Mass of crucible / g	32.2
Mass of crucible and hydrated barium chloride crystals / g	34.64
Mass of crucible and anhydrous barium chloride / g	34.28

(a)   State what is meant by the term hydrated in relation to crystalline substances.

....

(1 mark)

(b)   One of the results in the table has not been recorded correctly.
Identify this result and explain what is incorrect about the way it has been recorded.

Result: ....

Explanation: ....

(2 marks)

(c) (i) Calculate the mass of water given off during the heating of the hydrated salt.

mass of water = ... g

(1 mark)

(ii) Suggest how the student could have ensured that all of the water had been driven off.

....

(1 mark)

(d) Calculate the value of n in the formula $BaCl_2 . nH_2O$.

n = ...

(3 marks)

(e) Another student carries out the same experiment but loses some of the crystals from their crucible during heating. State whether this would make their value of n too high or too low. Explain your answer.

....

....

(1 mark)

3   A student carried out an experiment to identify an unknown Group 2 metal, **X**, by measuring the volume of hydrogen gas given off during the reaction of 0.14 g of **X** with excess hydrochloric acid. The equation for this reaction is: $X_{(s)} + 2HCl_{(aq)} \rightarrow XCl_{2(aq)} + H_{2(g)}$

The student set up the equipment as shown below, added the sample of metal **X** to the acid and replaced the bung on the conical flask.

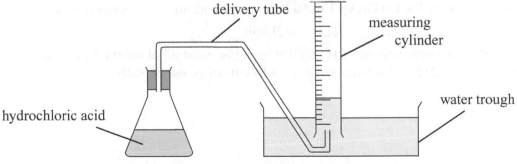

(a) The student carried out their experiment at room temperature and pressure.
The hydrogen gas given off was collected and found to have a volume of 138 cm³.
Use this information to help you identify metal **X**.

identity of metal **X** = ...

(3 marks)

(b) A second student used a similar method to identify a different metal, **Y**.
They reacted 0.0784 g of **Y** with excess sulfuric acid, according to the equation:

$$Y_{(s)} + H_2SO_{4(aq)} \rightarrow YSO_{4(aq)} + H_{2(g)}$$

The student used the same equipment to measure the volume of hydrogen
produced by the reaction. They determined that at a temperature
of 293 K and a pressure of 101 kPa, 28.9 cm³ of hydrogen was formed.

You can find any constants you need on the data sheet on pages 97-98.

Identify metal **Y**.

identity of metal **Y** = ...
(5 marks)

(c) Identify the major source of error in the method used by both students
and suggest an improvement to the method described.

Source of error: ....

Improvement: ....

....
(2 marks)

(d) This method can also be used to identify Group 1 metals by monitoring their
reaction with water. For the Group 1 metal lithium, the equation for this reaction is:

$$2Li_{(s)} + 2H_2O_{(l)} \rightarrow 2LiOH_{(aq)} + H_{2(g)}$$

Calculate the maximum volume of H_2 gas that would be given off at room temperature
and pressure if 0.0245 g of lithium metal was added to an excess of water.

volume of H_2 = ... cm³
(3 marks)

There will definitely be some questions to do with practical work in your exams. Conveniently,
you can practise for these every time you do an experiment in class. Remember to think
about what apparatus is most suitable for your experiments, how to control any variables that
might affect your results and how to present your results as clearly and neatly as possible.

Score

28

Amount of Substance, Acids and Redox — 4

1 Solutions of two different acids, sulfuric acid (H_2SO_4) and hydrochloric acid (HCl), are made up and put in unlabelled bottles. Both acids have the same unknown concentration.

(a) Explain how the identity of each acid could be determined by titration using a standard solution of 0.1 mol dm^{-3} sodium hydroxide (NaOH). Include in your answer the procedures involved, equations for any reactions taking place and the expected results.

....

....

....

....

....

....

....

....

....

....

....

....

....

....

....

....

....

(6 marks)

(b) Sulfuric acid reacts with magnesium metal to produce magnesium sulfate and hydrogen.

$$Mg_{(s)} + H_2SO_{4(aq)} \rightarrow MgSO_{4(aq)} + H_{2(g)}$$

(i) Explain, in terms of electron transfer, what is meant by the term oxidation.

....

(1 mark)

(ii) Use oxidation numbers to show which element in this reaction has been oxidised.

....

(1 mark)

(iii) Suggest what you would observe during this reaction.

....

....

....

(2 marks)

2 Limestone is an ore of calcium that contains a high proportion of calcium carbonate ($CaCO_3$).

Calcium carbonate reacts with hydrochloric acid according to the equation:

$$CaCO_3 + 2HCl \rightarrow CaCl_2 + CO_2 + H_2O$$

A 1.75 g sample of limestone is added to an excess of hydrochloric acid at a pressure of 101 kPa. 280 cm³ of carbon dioxide gas is formed at a temperature of 22.0 °C. It was assumed that all of the CO_2 gas produced was formed during the reaction between $CaCO_3$ and HCl.

(a) Calculate the percentage of $CaCO_3$ in the limestone sample.

Any constants you might need are on the data sheet on pages 97-98.

.... %

(5 marks)

(b) Calcium carbonate also reacts with ethanoic acid. Ethanoic acid is a weak acid.

(i) Explain what is meant by the term weak acid.

....

(1 mark)

(ii) Write a chemical equation for the reaction of calcium carbonate with ethanoic acid.

....

(1 mark)

(iii) Explain why calcium carbonate reacts more quickly with a 1 mol dm⁻³ solution of hydrochloric acid than with the same volume of 1 mol dm⁻³ ethanoic acid solution.

....

....

....

(2 marks)

(c) Calcium oxide is another calcium compound that will react with hydrochloric acid.

   (i) Write an equation for this reaction.

....

(1 mark)

   (ii) Identify the type of reaction occurring.

....

(1 mark)

   (iii) Explain, with reference to the oxidation numbers of the species
involved, whether or not this is classed as a redox reaction.

....

....

....

(1 mark)

3   Compound **C** is an example of a hydrated salt.

(a) Hydrated salts such as compound **C** contain water of crystallisation.
Explain what is meant by the term water of crystallisation.

....

....

(1 mark)

(b) Analysis of a 2.42 g sample of compound **C** found it to have the following composition by mass:

Mn, 0.668 g; Cl, 0.861 g; H, 0.097 g; O, 0.776 g

Deduce the formula of compound **C**. In your answer you should clearly show the water of crystallisation.

Formula of compound **C** = ...

(3 marks)

You're probably sick of hearing it by now but OIL RIG — Oxidation Is Loss, Reduction Is
Gain — is the most important thing to remember when you're thinking about redox reactions
in terms of movement of electrons. If you know where the electrons are coming from, and
where they're going to, you should hopefully be able to work everything else out from there...

Score

26

Electrons, Bonding and Structure — 1

Chemistry without electrons is like... Well there wouldn't *be* any chemistry without electrons. The shapes of molecules, the types of bonds that form where — all to do with electrons. Like this section, funnily enough.

For each of questions 1-5, give your answer by writing the correct letter in the box.

1   What is the electron configuration of titanium?

    A $1s^2\ 2s^2\ 2p^6\ 3s^2\ 3p^6\ 3d^4$ **B** $1s^2\ 2s^2\ 2p^6\ 3s^2\ 3p^6\ 3d^3\ 4s^1$

    C $1s^2\ 2s^2\ 2p^6\ 3s^2\ 3p^6\ 3d^2\ 4s^2$ **D** $1s^2\ 2s^2\ 2p^6\ 3s^2\ 3p^6\ 3d^3\ 4s^2$

Your answer ☐

(1 mark)

2   Which of these molecules is polar?

    A F_2 **B** CBr_4

    C CO_2 **D** PF_3

Your answer ☐

(1 mark)

3   Which of these molecules has a pyramidal shape?

    A CF_4 **B** BH_3

    C NCl_3 **D** SF_4

Your answer ☐

(1 mark)

4   Which row in the table below is correct?

| | Maximum number of electrons contained | | |
	3p sub-shell	3d orbital	3rd electron shell
A	2	10	18
B	6	10	18
C	6	2	18
D	6	2	8

Your answer ☐

(1 mark)

5   Which of the following ions have the electron configuration $1s^2\ 2s^2\ 2p^6\ 3s^2\ 3p^6$?

    A O^{2-} and Cl^- **B** Cl^- and Ca^{2+}

    C O^{2-} and Ca^{2+} **D** Cl^- and Na^+

Your answer ☐

(1 mark)

6   A chloride with the formula XCl_2 can be made by heating element X in chlorine gas.
The chloride has a high melting point and dissolves readily in water.
The chloride can conduct electricity when molten or in solution, but not when solid.

(a)   State the type of structure you would expect XCl_2 to have.

....

(1 mark)

(b)   Explain why XCl_2 has a high melting point.

....

....

(1 mark)

(c)   Explain how melting or dissolving XCl_2 enables it to conduct electricity.

....

....

(1 mark)

7   Ice is a crystalline substance.

(a)   Explain how hydrogen bonding arises between water molecules.
Include a diagram to show hydrogen bonding between two water molecules in your answer.

....

....

....

....

(4 marks)

(b)   Describe what happens to the molecules in ice when it is heated to its melting point.

....

....

(1 mark)

(c)   Explain why ice has a lower density than water.

....

....

....

(2 marks)

8   Sodium chloride, NaCl, and calcium chloride, $CaCl_2$, are examples of compounds with ionic bonding.

(a)   Explain what is meant by the term ionic bond.

....

(1 mark)

(b)   Draw a dot and cross diagram to show the bonding in solid calcium chloride,
showing outer shell electrons only.

(3 marks)

(c)   Write the electron configuration, in terms of sub-shells, of the sodium ion in NaCl.

....

(1 mark)

(d)   Describe the structure of an ionic compound using NaCl as an example.
You may include a diagram in your answer.

....

....

....

....

(4 marks)

(e)   The Pauling electronegativities of Na, Cl and H are given in the table below.

Element	Pauling electronegativity
Na	0.9
Cl	3.0
H	2.1

Using the information given, explain why NaCl has an ionic structure while HCl has a molecular structure.

....

....

....

....

(2 marks)

9   The table below gives the experimentally determined polarities of molecules of Br_2, CCl_4 and $CHCl_3$.

Molecule	Polarity
Br_2	Non-polar
CCl_4	Non-polar
$CHCl_3$	Polar

Explain the polarity, or lack of polarity, that these molecules have.
You may draw diagrams to support your answer.

....

....

....

....

....

....

....

....

....

....

....

....

(6 marks)

Electrons, Bonding and Structure — 2

1   In the atomic orbital model of the atom, electrons exist within fixed sub-shells.
These sub-shells contain atomic orbitals.

(a)   (i)   Explain the meaning of the term atomic orbital.

....

....

(2 marks)

The diagram below shows the shapes of two different types of atomic orbital.

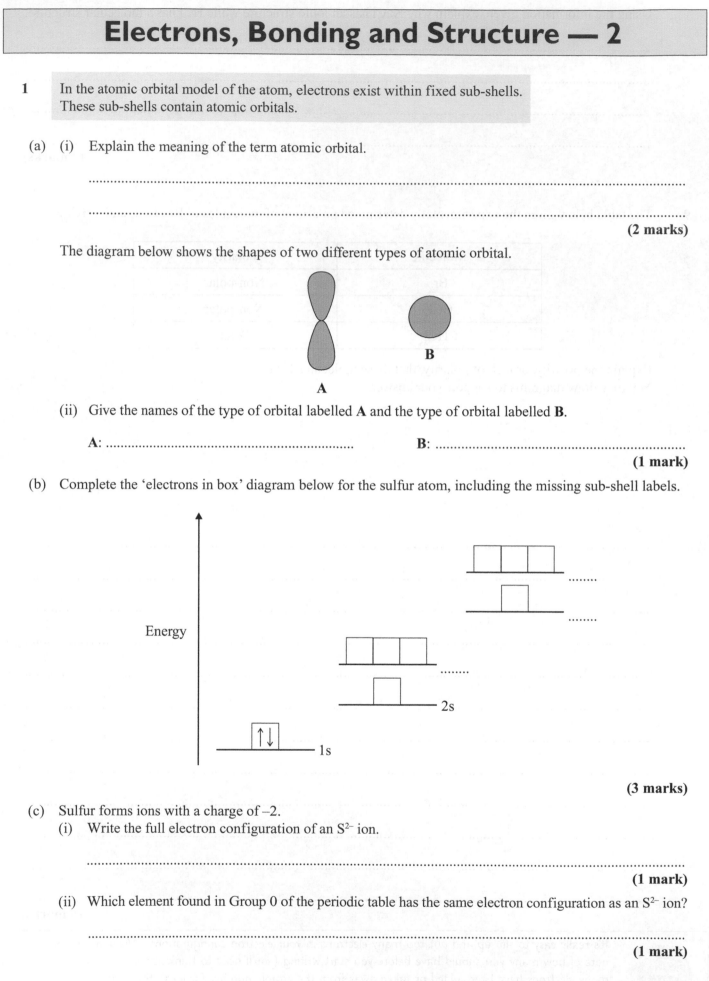

A

B

(ii)   Give the names of the type of orbital labelled **A** and the type of orbital labelled **B**.

A: ....   B: ....

(1 mark)

(b)   Complete the 'electrons in box' diagram below for the sulfur atom, including the missing sub-shell labels.

Energy

....

....

....

2s

↑↓   1s

(3 marks)

(c)   Sulfur forms ions with a charge of –2.
(i)   Write the full electron configuration of an S^{2-} ion.

....

(1 mark)

(ii)   Which element found in Group 0 of the periodic table has the same electron configuration as an S^{2-} ion?

....

(1 mark)

2 The graph below shows the boiling points of some of the Group 6 hydrides.

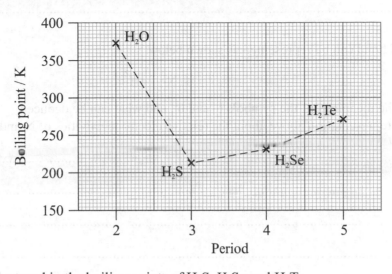

(a) Describe and explain the trend in the boiling points of H_2S, H_2Se and H_2Te.

....

....

....

(1 mark)

(b) Explain why the boiling point of H_2O is higher than expected

....

....

....

....

....

(3 marks)

3 Ammonium carbonate, $(NH_4)_2CO_3$, is made up of NH_4^+ and CO_3^{2-} ions. It was used as an early form of baking powder and commonly known as 'baker's ammonia'.

(a) In the NH_4^+ ion, the nitrogen atom is bonded to each of the four hydrogens.
Three of the bonds are single covalent and one is dative covalent.

(i) State what is meant by the term dative covalent bond.

....

(1 mark)

(ii) Draw a diagram to illustrate the 3-D shape of the NH_4^+ ion,
showing the different types of bond appropriately.

(2 marks)

Module 2 — Foundations in Chemistry

(b) (i) State the meaning of the term electronegativity.

....

(1 mark)

(ii) The N–H bond can be represented as shown below.

$$N^{\delta-}\!\!-\!\!H^{\delta+}$$

Explain the meanings of the symbols $\delta+$ and $\delta-$, and what can be deduced
from the representation above about the relative electronegativities of N and H.

....

....

....

....

(2 marks)

(c) The carbonate ion, CO_3^{2-}, also has covalent bonds. The carbon atom bonds to one oxygen atom with a
double covalent bond and to the other two oxygen atoms with single covalent bonds.
Draw a dot and cross diagram for the carbonate ion.
Show outer shell electrons only, using a different symbol for the two extra electrons.

(2 marks)

(d) Modern baking powder contains tartaric acid, the structure of which is shown in the diagram below.

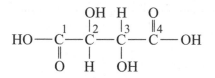

Use electron pair repulsion theory to explain the differences between the shape shown in this diagram and
the actual 3-D shape of a tartaric acid molecule. You may refer to the numbered carbon atoms in your answer.

....

....

....

....

....

....

(4 marks)

4   SF$_2$ and SF$_6$ are the formulae of two sulfur fluorides.

(a) (i)   Draw a diagram to show the shape of each molecule. Include any lone pairs around the central atoms
and indicate the values of the bond angles. Name the shapes you have drawn.

SF$_2$:   SF$_6$:

Shape of SF$_2$: ....

Shape of SF$_6$: ....

(4 marks)

(ii)   Explain the shape that you gave for SF$_2$.

....

....

....

....

(3 marks)

(b) The Pauling scale is a measure of electronegativity. On the Pauling scale, fluorine has an electronegativity
of 4.0 and sulfur has an electronegativity of 2.6. Explain why SF$_6$ is non-polar, but SF$_2$ is polar.

....

....

....

....

....

(4 marks)

(c) Explain why it is difficult to predict which of the two fluorides has the higher melting point.

....

....

....

....

(3 marks)

 EXAM TIP   You won't need to know any exact values for electronegativity for your exams, but it's helpful to
have an understanding of the overall trends in electronegativity moving around the periodic table.
Remember, electronegativity increases across periods and decreases down groups (ignoring the noble
gases), so the most electronegative elements (like fluorine and oxygen) are found at the top right.

Score

38

The Periodic Table — 1

The periodic table isn't just a creative way of listing the elements — you can use it to help you describe and explain all kinds of trends in their properties. Better get scrutinising it to answer the questions coming up...

For each of questions 1-4, give your answer by writing the correct letter in the box.

1　Which of these statements explains why metals have high melting points?

　　A　The atoms are closely packed.

　　B　There is a strong electrostatic attraction between the metal ions and the free electrons.

　　C　The atoms have a regular arrangement.

　　D　The positive metal ions repel each other.

　　Your answer ☐

(1 mark)

2　Which of the following halogens is the least reactive?

　　A　F_2　　　　　　　　　**B**　Cl_2

　　C　Br_2　　　　　　　　**D**　I_2

　　Your answer ☐

(1 mark)

3　Which of the following electron configurations is that of a d-block element?

　　A　$1s^2\,2s^2\,2p^6\,3s^2\,3p^6\,3d^{10}\,4s^2\,4p^5$

　　B　$1s^2\,2s^2\,2p^6\,3s^2\,3p^6\,3d^8\,4s^2$

　　C　$1s^2\,2s^2\,2p^6\,3s^2\,3p^6$

　　D　$1s^2\,2s^2\,2p^6\,3s^2\,3p^6\,3d^{10}\,4s^2\,4p^6\,5s^1$

　　Your answer ☐

(1 mark)

4　Which of the following statements about Group 2 elements is correct?

　　A　The first ionisation energy of the Group 2 elements increases going down the group.

　　B　The second ionisation energy is less than the first ionisation energy.

　　C　The first ionisation energy of a Group 2 element is greater
　　　　than that of the Group 1 element in the same period.

　　D　The first ionisation energy of a Group 2 element is less
　　　　than that of the Group 3 element in the same period.

　　Your answer ☐

(1 mark)

5   Graphite and graphene are both forms of carbon.

(a)   (i)   Describe the structure of graphite. Include a diagram to illustrate your answer.

Diagram:

Description: ....
....
....

(4 marks)

(ii)   Explain how the structures of graphite and graphene are related.

....
....

(1 mark)

(b)   (i)   Explain why graphite has a very high melting point.

....
....

(2 marks)

(ii)   Describe and explain the following properties of graphite.

Electrical conductivity:

....
....

Solubility:

....
....

(2 marks)

(c)   In the future, materials containing graphene could be used to make aircraft parts, because it is very light but extremely strong.
Explain why the structure of graphene makes it such a strong material.

....
....
....

(2 marks)

6   Magnesium reacts with chlorine to form the ionic compound magnesium chloride, $MgCl_2$.

(a)   (i)   Give the full electron configuration of a chlorine atom.

....

(1 mark)

     (ii)   Give the full electron configuration of a magnesium ion.

....

(1 mark)

(b)   Magnesium chloride can also be formed by the reaction of magnesium metal with hydrochloric acid.

     (i)   Write an equation for this reaction.

....

(1 mark)

     (ii)   Use oxidation numbers to show that this is a redox reaction.

....

....

....

(2 marks)

     (iii)   Strontium is below magnesium in Group 2 of the Periodic Table, and reacts more vigorously with hydrochloric acid than magnesium. Explain why strontium is more reactive than magnesium.

....

....

....

....

....

....

(4 marks)

(c)   Magnesium metal will react with water to produce magnesium hydroxide.

     (i)   Give one use of magnesium hydroxide.

....

(1 mark)

     (ii)   Suggest why magnesium hydroxide is **not** made industrially using the reaction of magnesium and water.

....

....

(1 mark)

Score

26

The Periodic Table — 2

1 Elements in the same groups or periods of the periodic table display patterns in their ionisation energies.

(a) State the meaning of the term first ionisation energy.

....

....

(1 mark)

The graph shows the first ionisation energies of the elements in Period 3.

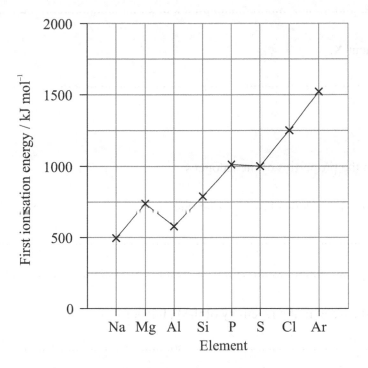

(b) State and explain **one** similarity and **one** difference between the graph shown above and a graph of the first ionisation energies of the Period 2 elements drawn on the same scale.

....

....

....

....

....

....

(4 marks)

(c) The table below shows the successive ionisation energies of an element, **X**, in Period 2 of the Periodic Table.

Ionisation energies / kJ mol^{-1}						
1st	2nd	3rd	4th	5th	6th	7th
1402	2856	4578	7475	9445	53268	64362

(i) Write an equation to represent the 2nd ionisation energy of element **X**.
Use **X** as the chemical symbol for the element and include state symbols.

....
(1 mark)

(ii) Suggest why the difference between the 5th and 6th ionisation energies of element **X** is so
much larger than that between the 4th and 5th ionisation energies. Explain your answer.

....

....

....

....
(3 marks)

(iii) Identify element **X**.

....
(1 mark)

2 There are trends in the properties of the halogens.

(a) Explain why chlorine has a lower boiling point than iodine.

....

....
(2 marks)

(b) State and explain the trend in the reactivity of the halide ions.

....

....

....
(4 marks)

(c) A more reactive halogen can displace a less reactive halogen from a solution of halide ions.
A student investigates this by adding an excess of chlorine water to a solution of potassium bromide.

(i) Write an ionic equation for the reaction that takes place.

....
(1 mark)

(ii) Identify which species is oxidised in the reaction.

....
(1 mark)

(iii) The student is given a pure solution of the potassium salt formed by the reaction.
When the student adds an aqueous solution containing silver ions to this solution, a precipitate forms.
State what colour you would expect the precipitate to be.

....
(1 mark)

3 The trend in the melting points across Period 3 is shown on the graph below.

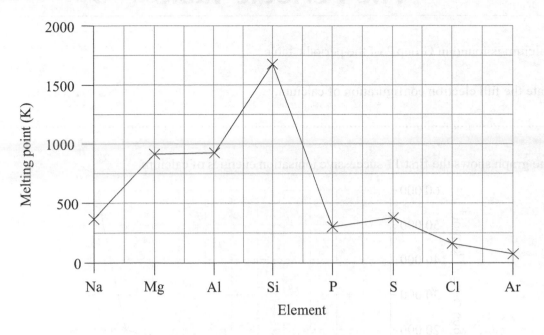

Describe and explain the patterns and variations in the melting points of the Period 3 elements shown on the graph. In your answer include ideas about the structure and bonding of the elements.

....

....

....

....

....

....

....

....

....

....

....

....

....

....

....

(6 marks)

When using atomic structure to describe patterns in reactivity or ionisation energy in the Periodic Table, you just need to think carefully about how each of three things change moving from element to element: the nuclear charge acting on the electrons, the distance of the outermost electrons from the nucleus, and the amount of shielding experienced by those outermost electrons.

Score

25

The Periodic Table — 3

1 Calcium is found in Group 2 of the periodic table.

(a) State the full electron configuration of calcium.

....
(1 mark)

The graph shows the first 11 successive ionisation energies of calcium.

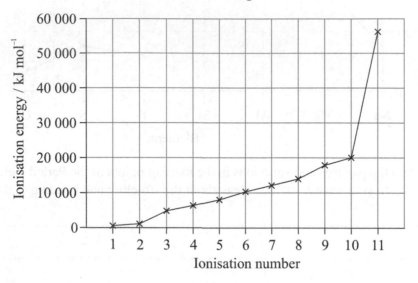

(b) Suggest why the second ionisation energy of calcium is greater than the first ionisation energy.

....

....

....
(2 marks)

(c) Explain how the graph shown provides evidence of the electron structure of a calcium atom.

....

....

....

....

....

....
(4 marks)

2 Group 2 metals are in the s-block of the periodic table.

(a) Explain, with reference to their electron configurations, why Group 2 metals
are classified as s-block elements.

....
(1 mark)

(b) (i) State and explain the trend in the reactivity of the Group 2 metals.

....

....

(1 mark)

(ii) Describe **one** similarity and **one** difference in the observations that you would expect to make when pieces of calcium and barium are added to water.

Similarity: ....

Difference: ....

(2 marks)

(c) The oxides of Group 2 metals also react with water.

(i) Write an equation, including state symbols, for the reaction of calcium oxide with water.

....

(2 marks)

(ii) Equal molar amounts of barium oxide and calcium oxide were added to two test tubes containing water. Which of the resulting solutions would have the highest pH? Explain your answer.

....

....

....

(3 marks)

3 Compounds containing chlorine are often used to disinfect water.
Reactions **1**, **2** and **3**, all involving chlorine compounds, are shown in the diagram below.

$$Cl_{2(g)} \xrightarrow[\textbf{2}]{NaOH_{(aq)}} NaClO_{(aq)} + NaCl_{(aq)} + \textbf{A}$$

$$\updownarrow \begin{array}{c} H_2O_{(l)} \\ \textbf{1} \end{array} \qquad\qquad \updownarrow \begin{array}{c} H_2O_{(l)} \\ \textbf{3} \end{array}$$

$$\begin{array}{c} HClO_{(aq)} \\ + \\ HCl_{(aq)} \end{array} \qquad\qquad \begin{array}{c} HClO_{(aq)} \\ + \\ \textbf{B} \end{array}$$

(a) (i) Write equations for reactions **2** and **3**, identifying the products A and B.

Reaction **2**: ....

Reaction **3**: ....

(2 marks)

(ii) Write an ionic equation for reaction **1**.

....

(1 mark)

(iii) Identify which of reactions **1-3** form a mixture of products containing chlorine in more than one oxidation state.

....

(1 mark)

(b) Describe **two** potential risks associated with using chlorine to treat public drinking water supplies.

1. ....

....

2. ....

....

(2 marks)

4   A student carried out some test tube reactions to investigate the reactions of the halogens with solutions of halide ions.

In experiment **1**, the student placed a sample of chlorine solution in a test tube and added the same volume of potassium bromide solution. She then repeated the procedure with a fresh sample of chlorine solution, this time adding potassium iodide solution.

The student then carried out experiments **2** and **3**, repeating the method used above using the combinations of halogen and halide solutions shown in the table below, and noting her observations.

	Experiment **1** $Cl_{2(aq)}$	Experiment **2** $Br_{2(aq)}$	Experiment **3** $I_{2(aq)}$
$KCl_{(aq)}$	✕		
$KBr_{(aq)}$	Yellow solution forms	✕	
$KI_{(aq)}$	Orange-brown solution forms		✕

(a) Complete the table to show the observations the student should have made for experiments **2** and **3**.

(2 marks)

(b) Identify the yellow solution formed in the reaction between chlorine solution and potassium bromide solution.

....

(1 mark)

(c) To make the colour changes easier to distinguish, the student shakes the reaction mixtures produced in experiment **1** with cyclohexane, an organic solvent. State and explain what would be observed in each case.

....

....

....

....

....

(4 marks)

(d) Write an ionic equation for the reaction between Cl_2 and KI and identify the oxidising agent in this reaction.

equation: ....

oxidising agent: ....

(2 marks)

(e) Sodium fluoride dissolves in water to form a colourless solution.
Suggest what you would observe if sodium fluoride solution and bromine solution were mixed.
Explain your answer.

....

....

(2 marks)

5 A student has a bottle labelled "sodium sulfate solution" and another labelled "sodium carbonate solution".
The student tests the solutions in both bottles to check that they contain the anions shown on the labels.

(a) (i) For the sulfate ion test, the student removed 5 cm³ of solution from the first bottle,
put it in a clean test tube and added a few drops of barium chloride solution.

Identify **one** additional step the student should have included when carrying out this test.
Explain why this may affect the result of the test.

....

....

....

(2 marks)

(ii) Describe a test that the student could have used to confirm the presence of
carbonate ions in the bottle labelled "sodium carbonate solution".

....

....

....

(3 marks)

(b) The student was given a third bottle which they were told contained either sodium bromide solution or
sodium iodide solution. They carried out a test to confirm which solution they had. The first part of the
test involved the formation of a silver halide. The second part involved trying to dissolve the silver halide.

Describe the test that the student used. Your answer should include a description of the results
that the student would have seen for each solution.

....

....

....

....

....

....

(5 marks)

Score

43

Physical Chemistry — 1

Bit of a mathsy section this, so better dust off your calculator, sharpen your pencil and find a ruler for those graphs...

For each of questions 1-4, give your answer by writing the correct letter in the box.

1   Consider this reaction: $2SO_{2(g)} + O_{2(g)} \rightleftharpoons 2SO_{3(g)}$ $\Delta H = -197$ kJ mol^{-1}
     Which of the following would shift the equilibrium in favour of the product the most?

   A   Decreasing the temperature and increasing the pressure.

   B   Decreasing the temperature and decreasing the pressure.

   C   Increasing the temperature and decreasing the pressure.

   D   Increasing the temperature and increasing the pressure.

   Your answer ☐

(1 mark)

2   Chloroethane can be produced by the reaction of ethene with hydrogen chloride gas.
$$C_2H_{4(g)} + HCl_{(g)} \rightarrow C_2H_5Cl_{(g)}$$
Some bond enthalpy data for this reaction is shown below.

Bond	C=C	C–H	H–Cl	C–C	C–Cl
Bond enthalpy / kJ mol^{-1}	612	413	432	347	346

What is the value of ΔH for the reaction?

   A   +85 kJ mol^{-1} **B**   −494 kJ mol^{-1}

   C   +351 kJ mol^{-1} **D**   −62 kJ mol^{-1}

   Your answer ☐

(1 mark)

3   250 cm^3 of 0.50 mol dm^{-3} sodium hydroxide solution was neutralised by an excess of hydrochloric acid.
     The total volume of the reaction mixture was 500 cm^3. The maximum temperature change was +3.5 °C.
     Calculate the molar enthalpy change of the reaction with respect to sodium hydroxide.
     You should assume that $c = 4.18$ J K^{-1}g^{-1}.

   A   −29 kJ mol^{-1} **B**   −59 kJ mol^{-1}

   C   +29 kJ mol^{-1} **D**   +59 kJ mol^{-1}

   Your answer ☐

(1 mark)

4   Which of the following statements about catalysts is true?

   A   Adding a catalyst will increase the yield from a reversible reaction.

   B   Catalysts increase the rate of reaction by offering an alternative reaction pathway with a higher energy.

   C   A catalyst is chemically unchanged at the end of a reaction.

   D   Adding a catalyst will decrease the value of K_c for a reversible reaction.

   Your answer ☐

(1 mark)

5 A student is investigating the energetics of the reaction shown in the following equation.

$$CuSO_{4(aq)} + Mg_{(s)} \rightarrow MgSO_{4(aq)} + Cu_{(s)}$$

(a) This reaction is exothermic.
   - Explain what is meant by this.
   - Illustrate your answer with a fully labelled enthalpy profile diagram to represent the enthalpy change for this reaction. You do not need to show the activation energy for the reaction.

....

....

Enthalpy

Progress of reaction

(4 marks)

(b) The student investigated the reaction experimentally by adding an excess of magnesium ribbon to 20 cm³ of 0.50 mol dm⁻³ copper(II) sulfate solution, $CuSO_{4(aq)}$, in a beaker and monitoring the temperature of the reaction mixture.

   (i) The student used a measuring cylinder with an uncertainty of 0.1 cm³ to measure out the $CuSO_{4(aq)}$. Calculate the percentage uncertainty in their measurement.

   percentage uncertainty = ... %
   (1 mark)

   (ii) Copper(II) sulfate solution is an irritant and is toxic to aquatic plants and animals. The student wore safety glasses and a lab coat when carrying out the experiment. Suggest **one** other precaution that the student should have taken to minimise the risk of using $CuSO_{4(aq)}$.

....

....

   (1 mark)

(c)   The student recorded a maximum temperature change of +55 °C over the course of the reaction.

Calculate a value for the enthalpy change of the reaction with respect to $CuSO_{4(aq)}$.
Assume the specific heat capacity of the mixture is 4.18 J K^{-1}g^{-1}.
Give your answer to an appropriate number of significant figures. Include units in your answer.

Enthalpy change of reaction = ...

(4 marks)

(d)   The experimentally determined value for the enthalpy change of
the reaction is different to the theoretical value under these conditions.

(i)   Suggest why this is the case.

....

(1 mark)

(ii)   Suggest **one** change the student could make to the experiment to make their result more accurate.

....

(1 mark)

6   Methanol has a number of important uses in the chemical industry.
It can be produced from carbon monoxide and hydrogen using the reaction shown below.

$$CO_{(g)} + 2H_{2(g)} \rightleftharpoons CH_3OH_{(g)} \qquad \Delta H = -90 \text{ kJ mol}^{-1}$$

This reaction is performed at high pressure and at a temperature of 250 °C.

(a)   This reaction can be described as a homogeneous reaction.
State what is meant by the term homogeneous reaction.

....

(1 mark)

(b)   Write the expression for the equilibrium constant, K_c, for this reaction.

....

(1 mark)

(c) Use le Chatelier's principle to explain why a high pressure is used for this reaction in industry.

....

....

....

....

(3 marks)

(d) (i) Increasing the temperature would increase the rate of the reaction.
Give **two** reasons why using a higher temperature would increase the rate of reaction.

....

....

....

(2 marks)

(ii) A catalyst is typically used for this reaction. This is so that the reaction can be carried
out at a relatively low temperature, but will still proceed at a reasonable rate.
In terms of the effect on the equilibrium position, explain why using a catalyst is
a better option than increasing the temperature to increase the rate of this reaction.

....

....

....

....

....

(3 marks)

(e) One of the main uses of methanol in industry is in the production of methanal (CH_2O).

$$2CH_3OH_{(l)} + O_{2(g)} \rightarrow 2CH_2O_{(l)} + 2H_2O_{(l)}$$

The table below shows the standard enthalpy changes of formation for the compounds in this reaction.

Compound	$CH_3OH_{(l)}$	$CH_2O_{(l)}$	$H_2O_{(l)}$
ΔH_f / kJ mol^{-1}	–239.1	–108.7	–285.8

Use the data provided to calculate the enthalpy change of the reaction under standard conditions.

Enthalpy change of reaction = ...kJ mol^{-1}

(2 marks)

Physical Chemistry — 2

1 Cobalt(II) acetate is used as a homogeneous catalyst in the industrial production of the plastic PET.

(a) (i) State the meaning of the term homogeneous catalyst.

....

(1 mark)

(ii) Explain the advantages in terms of environmental sustainability of using catalysts.

....

....

....

....

....

(3 marks)

(b) Cobalt(II) ions in water form a pink solution. The addition of chloride ions to cobalt(II) solutions results in the formation of a blue cobalt(II) chloride complex. An equilibrium is set up in a test tube where both cobalt species are present, as shown by the equation below.

$$Co^{2+}_{(aq)} + 4Cl^-_{(aq)} \rightleftharpoons [CoCl_4]^{2-}_{(aq)}$$
pink $\qquad\qquad$ blue

The colour of the equilibrium mixture is violet.

(i) Predict and explain the effect on the colour of the solution of increasing the concentration of chloride ions.

....

....

....

....

(2 marks)

(ii) Outline a qualitative method of investigating the effect of decreasing the temperature on the position of equilibrium.

....

....

(1 mark)

(iii) Describe and explain the observations you would expect to make during this investigation if the forwards reaction is endothermic.

....

....

....

(2 marks)

2   Magnesium reacts with hydrochloric acid to give magnesium chloride and hydrogen,
as shown by the equation below.

$$Mg_{(s)} + 2HCl_{(aq)} \rightarrow MgCl_{2(aq)} + H_{2(g)}$$

Some students are investigating how the rate of the reaction changes with temperature. To do this,
they add magnesium ribbon to 1 mol dm⁻³ hydrochloric acid and measure the volume of hydrogen
produced by the reaction over time. Then they repeat this procedure at different temperatures.

(a)   The results for the experiment performed at 30 °C are shown below.

Time / s	Volume of gas produced / cm³
0	0
10	15
20	25
30	30
40	28
50	35
60	35
70	35

(i)   On the grid below, draw a graph to represent the data provided. Include a line of best fit.

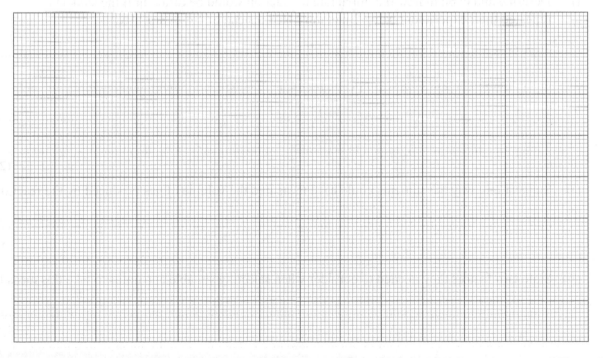

(3 marks)

(ii)   On your graph, circle any outliers in the data. Suggest **one** possible reason for any outliers.

....

....

(2 marks)

Module 3 — Periodic Table and Energy

44

(iii) Using your graph, calculate the initial rate of reaction, in cm³ s⁻¹, for the reaction performed at 30 °C. Show your working on the graph.

rate of reaction = ... cm³ s⁻¹

(2 marks)

(iv) Explain how collision theory can be used to predict how the rate of this reaction changes over time.

....

....

....

....

(2 marks)

(b) (i) Use your knowledge of the Boltzmann distribution to explain how increasing the temperature would affect the initial rate of reaction.

....

....

....

(2 marks)

(ii) Describe and explain how the initial rate of reaction would be different if the students repeated their experiment using 2 mol dm⁻³ HCl instead of 1 mol dm⁻³ HCl.

....

....

....

....

(2 marks)

(c) (i) Suggest **one** way the students could have measured the volume of gas produced by the reaction.

....

(1 mark)

(ii) State **two** factors they needed to consider when selecting suitable apparatus to take this measurement.

....

....

....

(2 marks)

There will definitely be some questions to do with practical work in your exams. The good news is that you can practise for these every time you do an experiment in class. Remember to think about what apparatus is most suitable for your experiments, how to control any variables that might affect your results and how to present your results as clearly and neatly as possible.

Score

25

Physical Chemistry — 3

1   Enthalpy changes during combustion can be investigated using theoretical and experimental methods.

(a)   A student is studying the complete combustion of propane, C_3H_8.
The equation for this reaction is shown below.

$$C_3H_{8(g)} + 5O_{2(g)} \rightarrow 3CO_{2(g)} + 4H_2O_{(g)}$$

(i)   The table below shows mean bond enthalpies for the bonds involved in this reaction.

Bond	C–C	C–H	C=O	O–H	O=O
Bond enthalpy / kJ mol^{-1}	347	413	805	464	498

Use the data provided to calculate the enthalpy of complete combustion of propane.

Enthalpy change of complete combustion = ... kJ mol^{-1}

(3 marks)

(ii)   The table below shows the enthalpies of formation of the compounds involved in the reaction.

Compound	$\Delta_f H$ / kJ mol^{-1}
$C_3H_{8(g)}$	–104.5
$CO_{2(g)}$	–393.5
$H_2O_{(g)}$	–241.8

Use this data to calculate the enthalpy of complete combustion of propane.

Enthalpy change of complete combustion = ... kJ mol^{-1}

(3 marks)

(iii) Explain why the value for the enthalpy of combustion of propane calculated using enthalpies of formation is not the same as the value calculated from mean bond enthalpies.

....

....

....

(2 marks)

(b) Another student decided to use calorimetry to investigate the complete combustion of propan-2-ol. They burned propan-2-ol in a spirit burner and recorded the change in the mass of the burner and the change in temperature of the water in the calorimeter. Their results are shown below.

Mass of burner before	75.2 g
Mass of burner after	74.8 g
Volume of water in calorimeter	50.0 cm³
Initial temperature of water	21.5 °C
Final temperature of water	74.0 °C

Calculate the enthalpy of complete combustion of propan-2-ol in kJ mol⁻¹.
The specific heat capacity of water is 4.18 J K⁻¹ g⁻¹.

Enthalpy change of complete combustion = ... kJ mol⁻¹

(5 marks)

2 When heated in air, potassium can react with oxygen to produce potassium peroxide, K_2O_2.
The overall equation for this reaction is:

$$2K_{(s)} + O_{2(g)} \rightarrow K_2O_{2(s)}$$

(a) Predict the effect of increasing the pressure on the rate of this reaction.
Explain your answer.

....

....

....

....

....

(4 marks)

(b) The Boltzmann distribution of the energies of the oxygen molecules in the reaction mixture at a given temperature is shown in the diagram below.

(i) Shade in the area on the distribution curve that corresponds to the number of oxygen molecules that are able to react with the potassium.

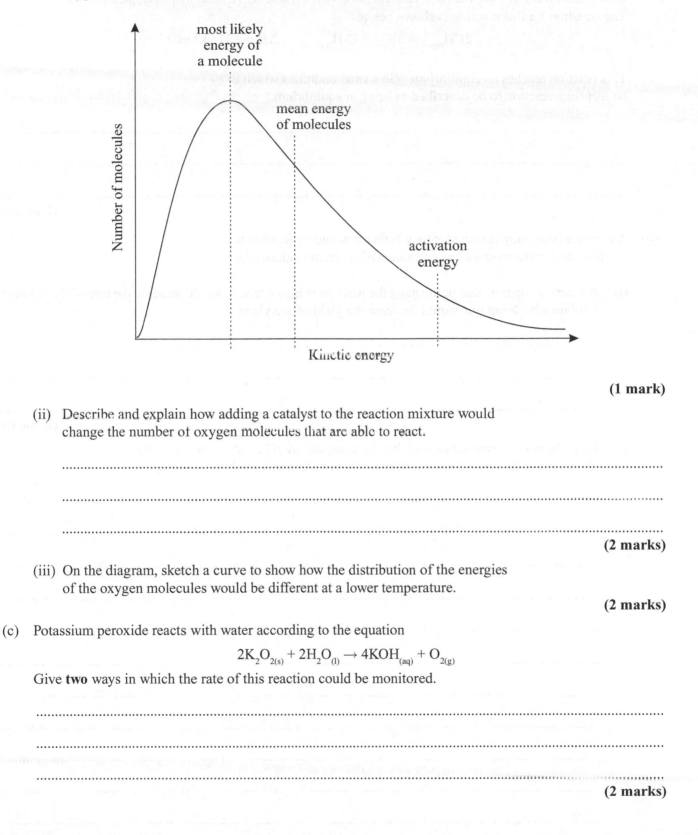

(1 mark)

(ii) Describe and explain how adding a catalyst to the reaction mixture would change the number of oxygen molecules that are able to react.

....

....

....

(2 marks)

(iii) On the diagram, sketch a curve to show how the distribution of the energies of the oxygen molecules would be different at a lower temperature.

(2 marks)

(c) Potassium peroxide reacts with water according to the equation

$$2K_2O_{2(s)} + 2H_2O_{(l)} \rightarrow 4KOH_{(aq)} + O_{2(g)}$$

Give **two** ways in which the rate of this reaction could be monitored.

....

....

....

(2 marks)

If you're asked to sketch a Boltzmann curve, don't spend too long fussing over the shape, or where exactly to mark the activation energy. Just make sure the start of the curve is at the origin, and the end doesn't flick up or touch the x-axis. Any wobbles in between shouldn't matter — the main thing is to show you understand the effect of any change in the conditions.

Score

24

Physical Chemistry — 4

1 Under certain conditions, methane can react to give acetylene (C_2H_2) and hydrogen gas. The equation for this reaction is shown below.

$$2CH_{4(g)} \rightleftharpoons 3H_{2(g)} + C_2H_{2(g)} \qquad \Delta H = +377 \text{ kJ mol}^{-1}$$

(a) This reaction reaches an equilibrium. Give **two** conditions which must be met for a reaction to be described as being at equilibrium.

....

....

....

(2 marks)

(b) A chemical company is considering whether it would be feasible to use this reaction to produce large amounts of acetylene industrially.

(i) A scientist suggests that performing the reaction at high pressure would increase the rate of the reaction. Explain why doing this would decrease the yield of acetylene.

....

....

....

(2 marks)

(ii) Describe and explain the factors that the company would need to consider when choosing an appropriate temperature for this reaction in an industrial setting.

....

....

....

....

....

....

....

....

....

....

....

....

....

(6 marks)

(c) (i) Write the expression for the equilibrium constant, K_c, for this reaction.

....

(1 mark)

(ii) A scientist performed a test experiment. They placed 1.00 moles of methane in a heatproof reaction vessel with a total volume of 3.00 dm³. The reaction vessel was then placed in a furnace at a very high temperature. The equilibrium mixture contained 0.372 moles of acetylene.

Calculate the value of K_c for this reaction using the information given above.
Give your answer to an appropriate number of significant figures.
Show **all** your working.

K_c =............................ mol² dm⁻⁶

(7 marks)

(iii) The scientist carried out a second test experiment, under different reaction conditions, and found that the value of K_c increased. Explain what this indicates about the position of equilibrium under these new reaction conditions, and what this means for the yield of acetylene.

....

....

(2 marks)

EXAM TIP

Remember, the rate of reaction and the position of equilibrium are separate. Exam questions often ask about the effect of increasing temperature, pressure and concentration, but their affect on rate is different to their affect on the position of equilibrium. So make sure you're clear which one you're being asked about.

Score

20

Basic Concepts and Hydrocarbons — 1

Organic chemistry is pretty tricky, but fear not — this section covers all the basics. Have a go at these questions, and you'll be a master of organic chemistry faster than you can say "smashed avocado with a side of chia seeds".

For each of questions 1-4, give your answer by writing the correct letter in the box.

1   What is the molecular formula of an alkane that contains 16 hydrogen atoms per molecule?

   A C_4H_8 B C_6H_{16}

   C C_7H_{16} D C_8H_{16}

   Your answer ☐

(1 mark)

2   The structures of four alkenes are shown below.

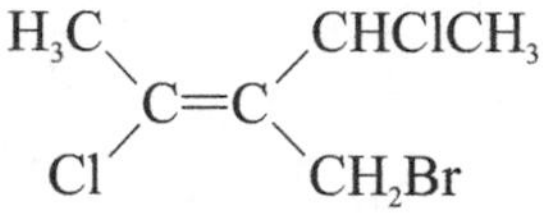

$$\underset{\textbf{M}}{\overset{H_3C}{\underset{Cl}{\diagdown}}C=C\overset{CHClCH_3}{\underset{CH_2Br}{\diagup}}} \qquad \underset{\textbf{N}}{\overset{F}{\underset{F}{\diagdown}}C=C\overset{H}{\underset{F}{\diagup}}} \qquad \underset{\textbf{O}}{\overset{FH_2C}{\underset{H_3C}{\diagdown}}C=C\overset{CH_2Br}{\underset{Cl}{\diagup}}} \qquad \underset{\textbf{P}}{\overset{H_3C}{\underset{Cl}{\diagdown}}C=C\overset{CH_2Br}{\underset{CHClCH_3}{\diagup}}}$$

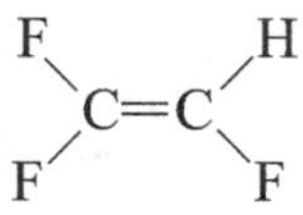

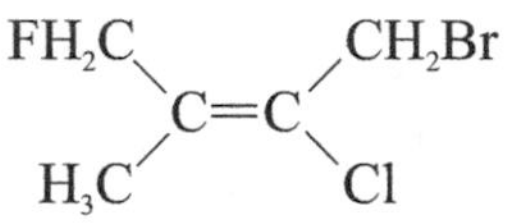

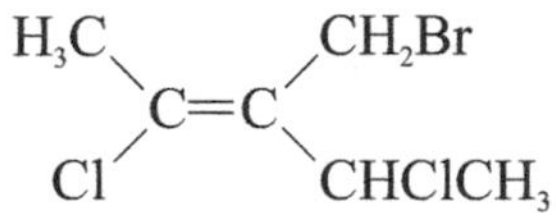

   Which of the alkenes above is a Z isomer?

   A   M   B   N

   C   O   D   P

   Your answer ☐

(1 mark)

3   Which of the following molecules does **not** exhibit E/Z stereoisomerism?

   A   3-methylpent-2-ene   B   2-methylbut-2-ene

   C   3-methylhex-2-ene   D   3-methylhex-3-ene

   Your answer ☐

(1 mark)

4   The molecule shown below is reacted with hydrogen bromide.

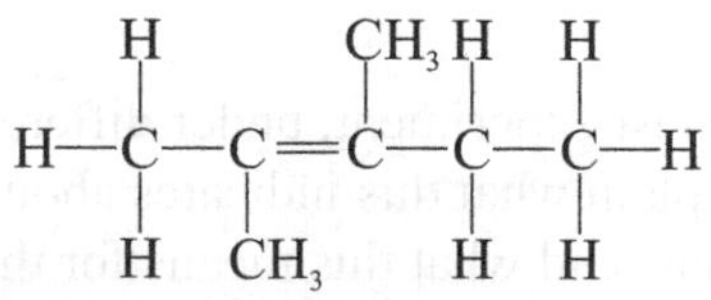

$$\overset{\displaystyle H \qquad CH_3\ H \quad H}{\underset{\displaystyle H \quad CH_3 \quad H\ H}{H-C-C=C-C-C-H}}$$

   Which of the following are the products of this reaction?

   A   4-bromo-3,4-dimethylpentane and 3-bromo-3,4-dimethylpentane.

   B   3-bromo-2,3-dimethylpentane and 2-bromo-2,3-dimethylpentane.

   C   3-bromo-2-methylpentane and 2-bromo-2-methylpentane.

   D   2-bromo-3,4-dimethylpentane and 3-bromo-2,3-dimethylpentane.

   Your answer ☐

(1 mark)

5 Hex-1-ene is a hydrocarbon with the molecular formula C_6H_{12}.
Four isomers of hex-1-ene are shown in the table.

Isomer	Displayed formula	Systematic name
A	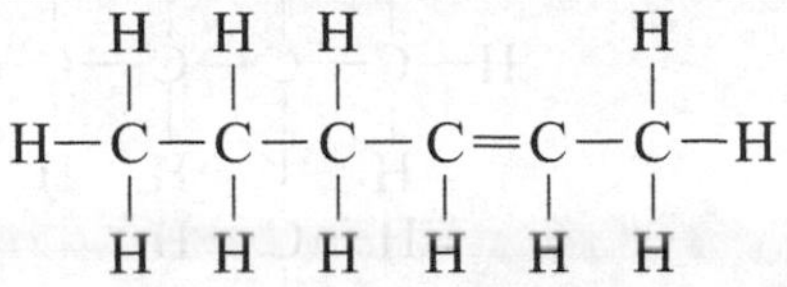	hex-2-ene
B	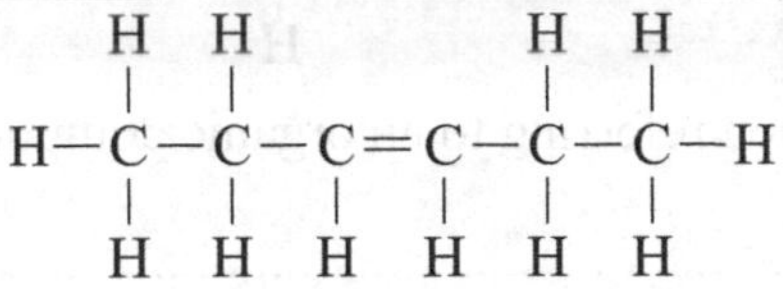	hex-3-ene
C		2,3-dimethylbut-1-ene
D	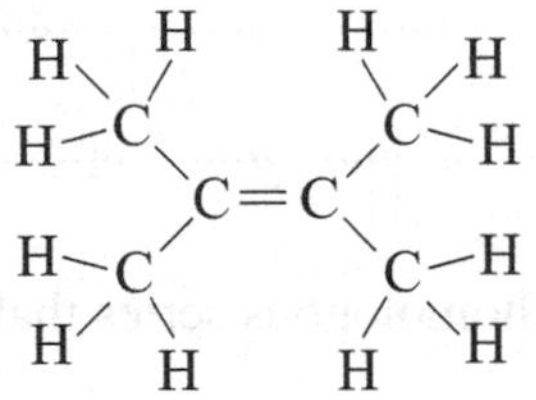	

(a) Write the letter of an isomer in the table that reacts with hydrogen to produce hexane.

....

(1 mark)

(b) Draw the displayed formula of isomer **C**.

(1 mark)

(c) State the systematic name of isomer **D**.

....

(1 mark)

(d) Draw the skeletal formula of a structural isomer of hex-1-ene
that does not contain the alkene functional group.

(1 mark)

6 The saturated organic compounds shown below are part of the same homologous series.

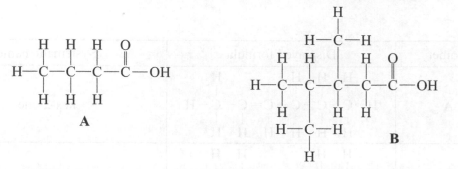

A

B

(a) State what is meant by the term 'saturated' when referring to an organic compound.

....

(1 mark)

(b) State **two** features of a homologous series.

....

....

(2 marks)

(c) Write the structural formula of the member of this homologous series that contains 2 carbon atoms.

....

(1 mark)

(d) State the systematic name of compound **B**.

....

(1 mark)

7 This question is about alicyclic hydrocarbons and haloalkanes.

Molecules **A** and **B** shown in the diagram below are both alicyclic.

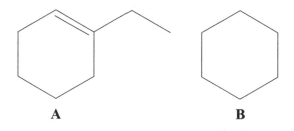

A   B

(a) (i) How many σ-bonds does molecule **A** have?

....

(1 mark)

(ii) Give the molecular formula of molecule **A**.

....

(1 mark)

(iii) Explain why molecules **A** and **B** are described as alicyclic.

....

....

(1 mark)

(b) Draw the displayed formula of a branched chain aliphatic saturated hydrocarbon that has the same number of carbon atoms as molecule **A**.

(1 mark)

(c) (i) Give the structural formula of an unsaturated structural isomer of molecule **B** that does not exhibit E/Z isomerism.

....

(1 mark)

(ii) Draw the skeletal formulae of **two** alicyclic saturated isomers of molecule **B**.

(2 marks)

(iii) Write the equation for the complete combustion of molecule **B**.
Use molecular formulae for all of the reactants and products.

....

(1 mark)

(d) The skeletal formulae of four haloalkanes, **C**, **D**, **E** and **F**, are shown below.

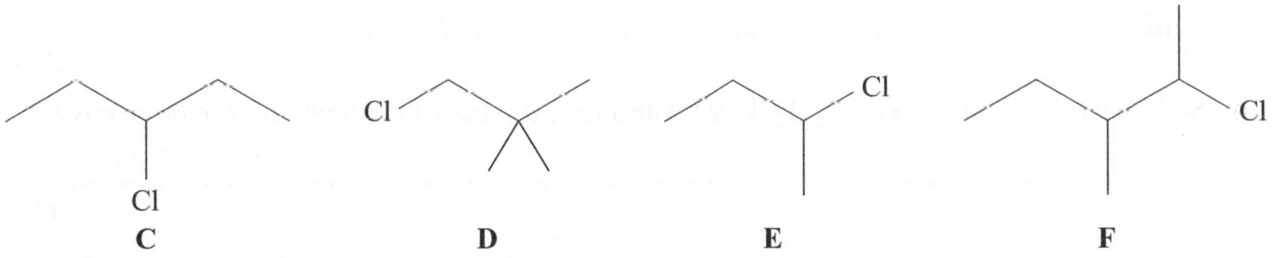

(i) Deduce the general formula of haloalkanes **C–F**.

....

(1 mark)

(ii) Which **two** of the haloalkanes are structural isomers?

....

(1 mark)

(iii) Give the systematic name of haloalkane **C**.

....

(1 mark)

EXAM TIP

There are quite a few definitions to learn in chemistry, but it's definitely worth memorising them. If you know your stuff, you'll be able to answer any questions that ask you for definitions quickly and easily in your exams. That will give you more time to answer the trickier questions.

Score

24

Basic Concepts and Hydrocarbons — 2

1   1,2-dichlorobut-1-ene ($C_4H_6Cl_2$) exists as a pair of stereoisomers.

(a)   Draw the Z isomer of 1,2-dichlorobut-1-ene.

(1 mark)

(b)   Explain why 1,2-dichlorobut-1-ene can exhibit E/Z stereoisomerism.

....

....

....

(2 marks)

(c)   Draw and name an isomer of $C_4H_6Cl_2$ other than 1,2-dichlorobut-1-ene, which exhibits
E/Z stereoisomerism. Your answer only needs to show the structure of **one** of the possible stereoisomers.

Name: ....

(2 marks)

(d)   State the name of an isomer of $C_4H_6Cl_2$ that is an alkene that does not exhibit E/Z stereoisomerism.

....

(1 mark)

2   This question is about polymers.

(a)   A section of an addition polymer is shown below.

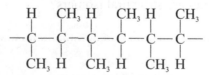

Draw and name the monomer used to form this polymer.

Monomer:

Name: ....

(2 marks)

Styrene acrylonitrile resin (SAN) is a copolymer, used in place of polystyrene where a greater thermal resistance is required. A copolymer is a polymer made from more than one type of monomer. The repeating unit of SAN is shown below.

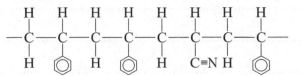

(b) (i) Draw the displayed formulae of the **two** monomers from which SAN is made.

(2 marks)

(ii) One of the monomers of SAN is an aromatic compound.
What is meant by the term aromatic compound?

....

(1 mark)

3 The diagram below shows the structure of ethene, the simplest alkene.

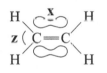

(a) (i) Identify the type of bond labelled **x**, and explain how this type of bond arises.

Type of bond: ....

Explanation: ....

....

(2 marks)

(ii) Predict the value of the bond angle marked **z**, and explain how this arises.

Bond angle: ....

Explanation: ....

....

(2 marks)

The diagram below shows the structure of another alkene, **A**.

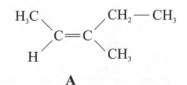

A

(b) Alkene **A** shows E/Z isomerism. Explain how Cahn-Ingold-Prelog priority rules can be used to deduce whether **A** is the E or Z isomer of the alkene. Include the full systematic name of alkene **A** in your answer.

....

....

....

....

....

....

....

....

....

(5 marks)

(c) (i) Explain why alkene **A** exhibits cis/trans isomerism.

....

....

(1 mark)

(ii) Alkene **B** is a structural isomer of alkene **A** that does **not** exhibit cis/trans isomerism. Draw **one** possible structure for alkene **B**.

(1 mark)

(d) Alkene **A** can be reacted with hydrogen in the presence of a nickel catalyst.
(i) Draw the skeletal formula of the product formed in this reaction.

(1 mark)

(ii) Explain why the product of the reaction in (i) is less reactive than alkene **A**.

....

....

(1 mark)

(e) Alkenes can also react with water to form alcohols. Two different alcohols can be formed from alkene **A**. Write an equation to show the formation of the major alcohol product from alkene **A**, showing the structures of any organic reactants and organic products. State the necessary reaction conditions.

Reaction conditions: ....

(2 marks)

4   Excess 1-methylcyclohexene reacts with bromine water in the reaction shown below.

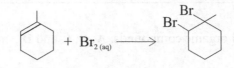

(a) Describe the change you would expect to see in the bromine water during the reaction.

....

(1 mark)

(b) Explain why alkenes are attacked by electrophiles.

....

(1 mark)

The mechanism involves the formation of a carbocation intermediate.
There are two possible carbocations, **A** and **B**, that can be formed.

(c) Draw curly arrows on the diagram below to show how the carbocation intermediates are formed.

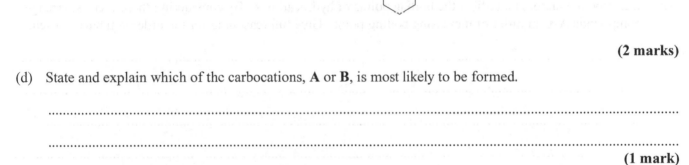

(2 marks)

(d) State and explain which of the carbocations, **A** or **B**, is most likely to be formed.

....

....

(1 mark)

(e) 1-methylcyclohexene also reacts with hydrogen bromide.
     Draw the skeletal formulae of the **two** products formed in this reaction.

(2 marks)

Score

33

Basic Concepts and Hydrocarbons — 3

1   The structures of four saturated organic compounds, **A**, **B**, **C** and **D** , are shown below.

$$CH_3(CH_2)_2CH_3 \qquad H_3C - \underset{\underset{CH_3}{|}}{\overset{\overset{CH_3}{|}}{C}} - H \qquad \bigwedge\!\!\bigwedge \qquad H_3C - \underset{\underset{CH_3}{|}}{\overset{\overset{CH_3}{|}}{C}} - Cl$$

A   **B**   **C**   **D**

(a) (i)   Use electron pair repulsion theory to predict the bond angle and
           the shape of the bonds around the central carbon atom in compound **B**.

   Bond angle: ....

   Shape: ....

   (2 marks)

   (ii) Draw the skeletal formula of compound **B**.

   (1 mark)

(b)* Describe the factors that affect the boiling points of hydrocarbons. By considering these factors, arrange
     compounds **A-C** in order of increasing boiling point. Give full reasoning for the order you have chosen.

   ....

   ....

   ....

   ....

   ....

   ....

   ....

   ....

   ....

   ....

   ....

   ....

   ....

   (6 marks)

The enthalpies of some of the bonds and the electronegativities of
the atoms found in compounds **A-D** are shown in the tables below.

Bond	Enthalpy / kJmol^{-1}
C – Cl	346
C – H	413

Atom	Electronegativity
C	2.5
Cl	3.0
H	2.1

(c) Using the information given in the tables, state and explain which compound, **B** or **D**, is more reactive.

....

....

....

....

....

....

(3 marks)

The electronegativity of the atoms in a bond determines
whether it breaks by homolytic fission or heterolytic fission.

(d) (i) Describe the difference between homolytic and heterolytic fission.

....

....

....

(2 marks)

(ii) Give the structural formulae of the **two** species formed when
the C–Cl bond in molecule **D** breaks by heterolytic fission.

....

(1 mark)

2 Synthetic polymers produced from alkenes are non-biodegradable and
therefore need to be disposed of carefully at the end of their lifetime.

(a) (i) PVC is made from the monomer chloroethene. One of the synthetic routes to chloroethene involves
the formation of 1,2-dichloroethane from chlorine and ethane in a photochemical reaction.
Using structural formulae, write equations to show a possible mechanism for this reaction
that involves **one** initiation step, **three** propagation steps and **one** termination step.

Initiation: ....

Propagation step 1: ....

Propagation step 2: ....

Propagation step 3: ....

Termination: ....

(5 marks)

Module 4 — Core Organic Chemistry

(ii) Give **two** reasons why 1,2-dichloroethane is not the only organic product of this reaction.

....

....

....

....

(2 marks)

(b) Waste PVC can be processed in an incinerator using a combustion reaction.

(i) Describe **two** benefits for sustainability of disposing of PVC in this way.

....

....

....

....

(2 marks)

(ii) Waste PVC can also be used as an organic feedstock to produce new polymers.
Suggest **one** benefit for sustainability of processing PVC in this way, rather than using combustion.

....

....

(1 mark)

Scientists are trying to develop biodegradable and photodegradable polymers in order to reduce plastic waste.

(c) (i) Describe and explain **two** benefits to the environment of
biodegradable plastics, compared to plastics such as PVC.

....

....

....

....

....

(4 marks)

(ii) State and explain what is needed in the environment to break down biodegradable
and photodegradable polymers.

....

....

....

(2 marks)

Score

31

Alcohols, Haloalkanes and Analysis — 1

Alcohols and haloalkanes have already put in guest appearances in some of the reactions that have come up earlier in this module. Now they're ready to take centre stage.

For each of questions 1-4, give your answer by writing the correct letter in the box.

1   A student measured the time taken for a precipitate to form when a solution of silver nitrate was added to test tubes containing equal volumes and concentrations of one of 1-chlorobutane, 1-iodobutane and 1-bromobutane dissolved in ethanol. Her results are shown below.

Haloalkane	Time taken for precipitate to form / s
1-chlorobutane	588
1-iodobutane	
1-bromobutane	88

Predict how long it took for a precipitate to form in the test tube containing 1-iodobutane.

A   330 seconds   B   50 seconds

C   120 seconds   D   810 seconds

Your answer ☐

(1 mark)

2   Which of the following compounds could be distinguished from the other three using molecular ion data from mass spectrometry?

A $NH_2CH_2CH_2NH_2$ B $CH_3CH_2CH_2OH$

C CH_3COCH_3 D CH_3COOH

Your answer ☐

(1 mark)

3   Which of the following shows an alcohol which can undergo oxidation but not elimination of water?

A
```
     H   CH₃  H
     |    |   |
 H—C—C—C—OH
     |    |   |
     H   CH₃  H
```

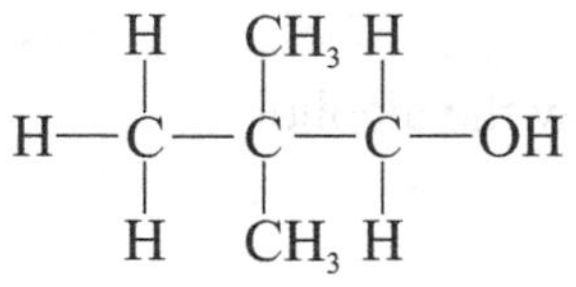

B
```
     H   CH₃  H   H
     |    |   |   |
 H—C—C—C—C—H
     |    |   |   |
     H   CH₃  OH  H
```

C
```
     H   OH   H
     |    |   |
 H—C—C—C—H
     |    |   |
     H   CH₃  H
```

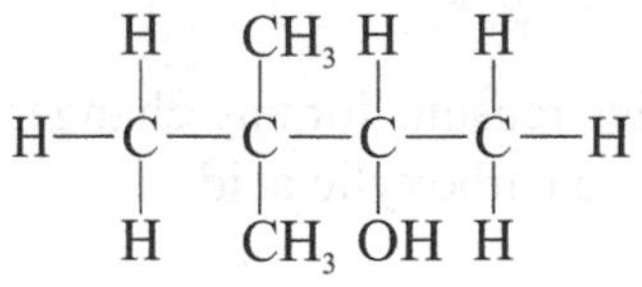

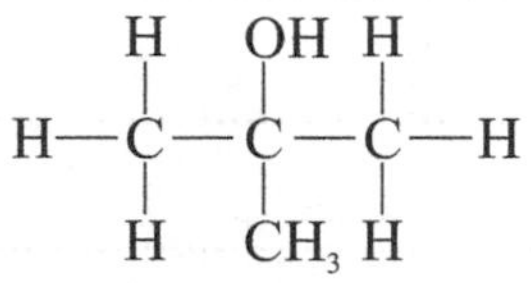

D
```
     H    H   H   H
     |    |   |   |
 H—C—C—C—C—H
     |    |   |   |
     H    H   OH  H
```

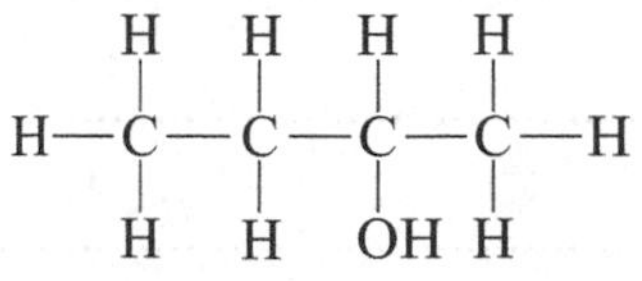

Your answer ☐

(1 mark)

4   The infrared spectrum of compound **X** shows a peak at wavenumber 1700-1725 cm^{-1} and a broad peak at wavenumber 3240-3280 cm^{-1}. Use the data sheet on pages 97-98 to help you determine which of the following functional groups could have caused these peaks.

A   C–C and C=O   B   COOH

C   C–O and O–H   D   C=C and C=O

Your answer ☐

(1 mark)

5 The apparatus shown below can be used to oxidise an alcohol to an aldehyde.

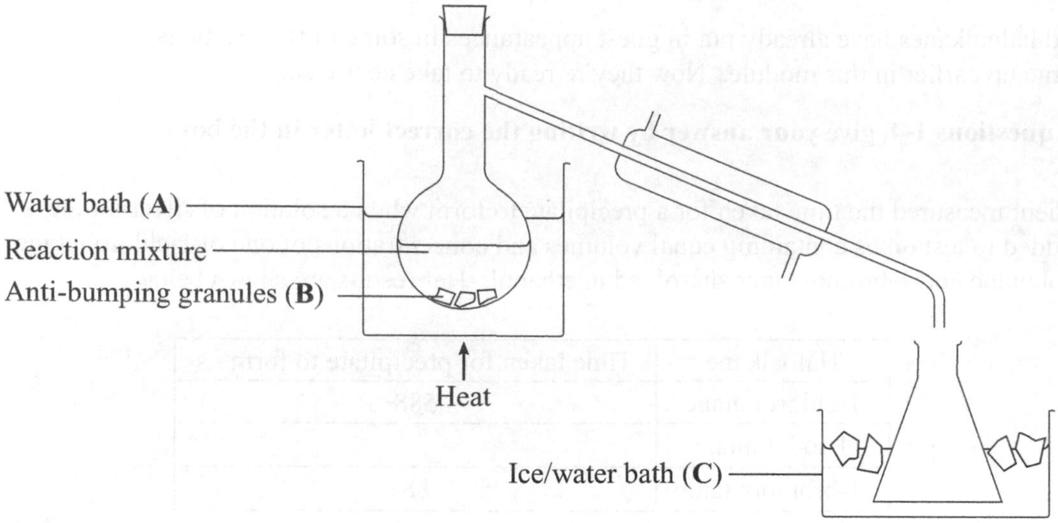

Water bath (**A**)

Reaction mixture

Anti-bumping granules (**B**)

Heat

Ice/water bath (**C**)

(a) The reaction mixture contains ethanol, sulfuric acid and an excess of an oxidising agent.
Name a suitable oxidising agent for this reaction.

....

(1 mark)

(b) Identify the method shown in the diagram and explain how it allows a pure sample of an aldehyde
to be prepared from an alcohol.

....

....

(2 marks)

(c) Suggest the purpose of the parts of the practical set-up labelled **A** to **C**.

A: ....

B: ....

C: ....

(3 marks)

(d) Describe and give reasons for any changes in the set-up that would allow the alcohol
to be oxidised to a carboxylic acid.

....

....

....

(3 marks)

(e) Write an equation to show how ethanol is oxidised to ethanoic acid.
You should represent the oxidising agent as [O] in your answer.

....

(1 mark)

6   Alcohols can be classified as primary, secondary or tertiary.

(a)   Draw the displayed formula for each of the following compounds.
Classify each of the compounds as a primary, secondary or tertiary alcohol.
(i)   2-methylbutan-2-ol

Class of alcohol: ....

(2 marks)

(ii)   2-methylpentan-3-ol

Class of alcohol: ....

(2 marks)

Alcohols can be useful as fuels, because they undergo combustion reactions.

(b)   Write an equation for the complete combustion of pentan-1-ol.

....

(1 mark)

(c)   The boiling points and solubilities for ethane and ethanol are shown in the table below:

	Boiling point / °C	Solubility in water
Ethane	−89	Insoluble
Ethanol	78	Very soluble

(i)   Identify the types of intermolecular force present for each compound, and use them to explain the differences between the boiling points of ethane and ethanol.

....

....

....

....

(3 marks)

(ii)   Suggest and explain what happens to the solubility of alcohols as the carbon chain increases in length.

....

....

....

(1 mark)

64

(d) Under acidic conditions, 3-methylbutan-2-ol reacts with sodium chloride to produce an organic product and an inorganic product.

Draw the displayed formula of the organic product formed, and give its name.

Name: ....

(2 marks)

7 Haloalkanes can undergo nucleophilic substitution reactions with a variety of nucleophiles.

(a) Give the meaning of the term nucleophile.

....

(1 mark)

When a warm aqueous solution of potassium hydroxide is added to iodoethane, a nucleophilic substitution reaction occurs producing ethanol and an iodide ion.

(b) (i) Identify the nucleophile in this reaction.

....

(1 mark)

(ii) Draw the mechanism for this nucleophilic substitution reaction. Include curly arrows and indicate any relevant dipoles.

(3 marks)

(iii) Explain why ethane does not react with potassium hydroxide.

....

....

(1 mark)

Haloalkanes containing multiple halogen atoms can also undergo nucleophilic substitution reactions.

(c) Name the organic compound formed when 2,3-dichlorohexane undergoes a nucleophilic substitution reaction with excess aqueous sodium hydroxide.

....

(1 mark)

When you're drawing mechanisms, make sure you're really careful with those curly arrows. To get the marks, the arrows need to go from a bond, a lone pair of electrons or a negative charge. Make sure you show all the relevant positive and negative charges and dipoles correctly.

EXAM TIP

Score

32

Module 4 — Core Organic Chemistry

Alcohols, Haloalkanes and Analysis — 2

1   The displayed formula for compound **B** is shown below.

$$H-\underset{\overset{\displaystyle |}{\underset{\displaystyle \|}{}}}{C}H - \underset{\overset{\displaystyle |}{\underset{\displaystyle H}{}}}{C} = \underset{\overset{\displaystyle |}{\underset{\displaystyle H}{}}}{C} - \underset{\overset{\displaystyle |}{\underset{\displaystyle H}{}}}{C} - \underset{\overset{\displaystyle |}{\underset{\displaystyle H}{}}}{C} - O - H$$

Compound **B**

(a)   Name the functional groups present in compound **B**.

....

....

(1 mark)

(b)   Identify and explain the types of reaction that occur, along with the expected observations made, when each of the following reagents are added to a sample of compound **B**:

(i)   Bromine water at room temperature

....

....

(2 marks)

(ii)   Acidified potassium dichromate(VI) whilst heating under reflux

....

....

(2 marks)

(c)   Alcohols can be converted into alkanes via a two-stage synthesis.
An example using propan-2-ol is shown below.

$$\text{propan-2-ol} \xrightarrow{\text{Stage 1}} \text{propene} \xrightarrow{\text{Stage 2}} \text{propane}$$

Name the type of reaction, the reagents and the conditions required for each stage of the synthesis.

(i)   Stage 1:

Type of reaction: ....

Reagents and conditions: ....

....

(2 marks)

(ii)   Stage 2:

Type of reaction: ....

Reagents and conditions: ....

....

(3 marks)

2 Infrared spectroscopy is a commonly used method of analysing compounds.

(a) Explain how the infrared spectra for water vapour, carbon dioxide and methane could be used to provide evidence for the fact that these compounds act as greenhouse gases.

....

....

....

....

....

(3 marks)

(b) Infrared spectroscopy is used to test for ethanol in the breath of drivers suspected of drink-driving. Suggest why this test focuses on the C–H bond in the ethanol molecules instead of the OH group.

....

....

(1 mark)

Compound **I** is one of butanol, butanal or but-2-ene. It was analysed using infrared spectroscopy to determine its identity. The spectrum produced is shown below.

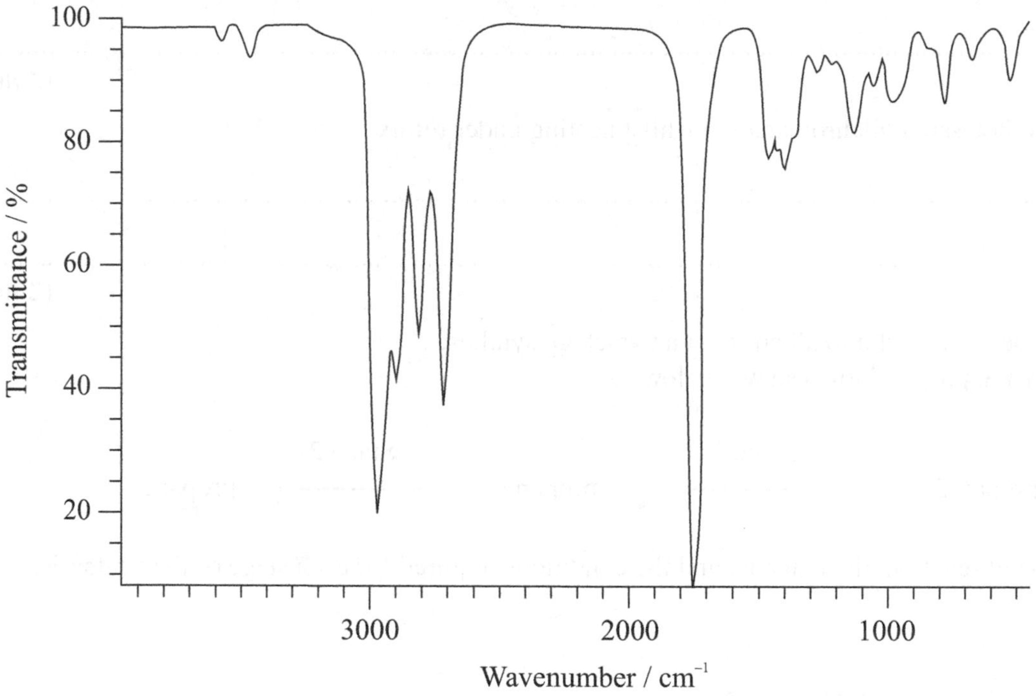

(c) Use the spectrum and the infrared absorption data given on the data sheet on pages 97-98 to identify compound **I** as either butanol, butanal or but-2-ene. Give full reasoning for your answer.

....

....

....

....

....

(4 marks)

3 In the presence of water, haloalkanes undergo nucleophilic substitution reactions to form an alcohol and a halide ion. These types of reactions are also known as hydrolysis reactions.

(a) Suggest why the reaction with water is slower than other nucleophilic substitution reactions of haloalkanes.

....

(1 mark)

The bond enthalpies of the carbon-halogen bonds are shown below:

Bond	C–F	C–Cl	C–Br	C–I
Bond enthalpy / kJ mol^{-1}	467	346	290	228

(b) Use the data to predict and explain the trend in the rates of hydrolysis of the carbon-halogen bonds.

....

....

....

(2 marks)

The rate of hydrolysis of different carbon-halogen bonds can be compared experimentally using water in the presence of silver nitrate and ethanol.

(c)* Describe the method used to investigate the trend in the rate of hydrolysis of 1-chlorobutane, 1-bromobutane and 1-iodobutane. Your answer should include:

- an explanation of what steps are taken to ensure that the experiment is a fair comparison of the carbon-halogen bonds present,
- general equations for the reactions that take place, using X to represent a halogen.

....

....

....

....

....

....

....

....

....

....

....

(6 marks)

EXAM TIP There are lots of reactions in the organic section of this course — and you might well get a question that asks you to put two of them together in an unfamiliar way. If you need to find a route from one compound to another and you haven't a clue how to get there, just keep calm and start by thinking what you do know about the reactions of the initial compound.

Score

27

Alcohols, Haloalkanes and Analysis — 3

1   A student plans to prepare a pure sample of 1-bromobutane from butan-1-ol and potassium bromide.

In the first stage of the experiment the reaction mixture is shaken in a sealed flask.
The mixture contains butan-1-ol, aqueous potassium bromide solution and a third reagent.

(a)   Suggest the identity of the third reagent.

....

(1 mark)

After shaking, the reaction mixture contains 1-bromobutane, and may also contain unreacted reagents.
1-bromobutane is insoluble in water. It is also more dense than water.

(b)   Name a piece of equipment that can be used to remove any water-soluble impurities from the reaction
mixture, and describe how it is used.

....

....

....

....

....

(4 marks)

The impure 1-bromobutane removed from the reaction mixture may still contain traces of water, which must
be removed using a drying agent. At the end of the drying process, the drying agent must also be removed.

(c)   Name a suitable drying agent and suggest how it can be removed from the 1-bromobutane.

....

....

(2 marks)

Once the drying agent has been removed from the 1-bromobutane, there may still be impurities remaining.

(d)   Name and describe a technique that could be used to remove any liquid impurities remaining and allow
pure 1-bromobutane to be collected.

....

....

....

....

....

....

....

(6 marks)

e)   Suggest **two** reasons why the percentage yield for this preparation is not 100%.

....

....

(2 marks)

2   Organic compound **X** is a liquid with an unknown identity. The identity and structure of compound **X** can be determined by combining information gathered from different methods of analysis.

The mass spectrum of compound **X** is shown below.

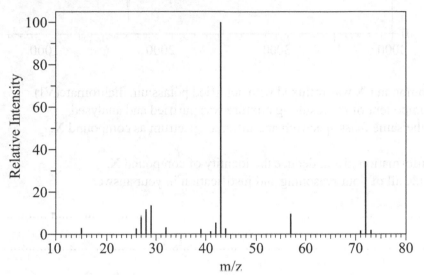

The molecular ion peak on the mass spectrum of compound **X** has a mass/charge (m/z) value of 72.
There is also a smaller peak, the M+1 peak, at a mass/charge value of 73.

(a) Explain why this M+1 peak is present.

....

(1 mark)

(b) State what information about organic compound **X** is given by the value of the molecular ion peak.

....

(1 mark)

Combustion analysis showed that the composition by mass of compound **X**
is 66.7% carbon, 11.1% hydrogen and 22.2% oxygen.

(c) Use this data to deduce the empirical formula of compound **X**.

(2 marks)

An infrared spectrum for compound **X** was also produced. This spectrum is shown below.

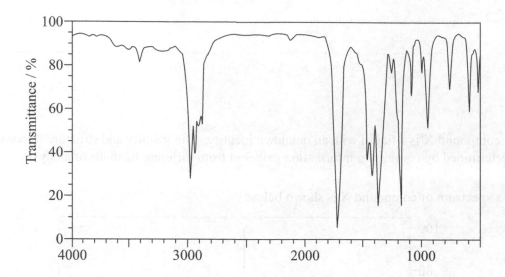

A sample of compound **X** was refluxed with acidified potassium dichromate(VI). The organic component of the resulting mixture was purified and analysed, and produced the same mass spectrum and infrared spectrum as compound **X**.

(d)* Using all the information given, deduce the identity of compound **X**. You must include all of your reasoning and justification in your answer.

....

....

....

....

....

....

....

....

....

....

....

....

....

(6 marks)

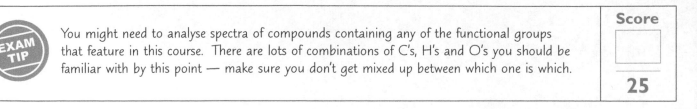

Score

25

You might need to analyse spectra of compounds containing any of the functional groups that feature in this course. There are lots of combinations of C's, H's and O's you should be familiar with by this point — make sure you don't get mixed up between which one is which.

Mixed Questions — 1

I hope you had a large helping of your wholegrain, wheat-based, high-fibre breakfast cereal this morning, because this section will test you on material from Modules 2, 3 and 4. It's time to bring it all together.

For each of questions 1-4, give your answer by writing the correct letter in the box.

1   Which statement about chemical reactions is correct?

    A   Magnesium reacts more vigorously than barium with water.

    B   Adding a catalyst means that, on average, the reactant molecules have more kinetic energy.

    C   Reactant molecules move slower at higher temperatures.

    D   Increasing the temperature shifts the Boltzmann distribution curve to the right.

Your answer ☐

(1 mark)

2   What is the chemical equation for the 2nd ionisation energy of sulfur?

    A $S_{(g)} \rightarrow S^{2+}_{(g)} + 2e^-$ **B** $S^+_{(g)} \rightarrow S^{2+}_{(g)} + e^-$

    C $S^{2+}_{(g)} + e^- \rightarrow S^+_{(g)}$ **D** $S^{2+}_{(g)} \rightarrow S^{3+}_{(g)} + e^-$

Your answer ☐

(1 mark)

3   What is the oxidation number of hydrogen in MgH_2?

    A   +2   **B**   +1

    C   −1   **D**   −2

Your answer ☐

(1 mark)

4   Which compound could be produced if 2-bromopentan-3-ol was heated with aqueous NaOH?

    A   2,3-dibromopentane

    B   2-bromopentane-2,3-diol

    C   pentane-2,3-diol

    D   2-bromopentan-3-one

Your answer ☐

(1 mark)

5 A student is investigating the rate of the reaction between calcium and water.

She uses the following method:

1. Add 150 cm³ of water to a conical flask.
2. Add 142 mg of calcium to the conical flask and connect a 100 cm³ gas syringe.
3. Use a stopwatch to record the time taken for 80 cm³ of gas to be produced.

The reaction is carried out at a pressure of 100 kPa and a temperature of 298 K.

(a) The reaction of calcium with water is an example of a redox reaction.
Write a half-equation for the oxidation process occurring during the reaction.

....
(1 mark)

(b) Give the oxidation number of hydrogen in a molecule of water.

....
(1 mark)

(c) Use the ideal gas equation to calculate the maximum mass of calcium that the student could use without exceeding the capacity of the gas syringe.
Give your answer to an appropriate number of significant figures.

mass = ... mg
(5 marks)

(d) Suggest why the amount of gas collected during the experiment may be less than the amount of gas produced during the reaction.

....

....
(1 mark)

(e) The student repeats the experiment twice more, but uses strontium and barium instead of calcium.
Predict which metal produced 80 cm³ of gas in the shortest time. Justify your answer.

....

....
(2 marks)

6 The industrial production of aluminium chloride ($M_r = 133.5$) involves heating aluminium metal with chlorine at a temperature of 750 °C.

The equation for the reaction is:

$$2Al + 3Cl_2 \rightarrow 2AlCl_3$$

(a) Write the electron configuration, in terms of sub-shells, of an aluminium atom.

....
(1 mark)

(b) Give the oxidation number of aluminium and chlorine in aluminium chloride.

Aluminium oxidation number: ....   Chlorine oxidation number: ....
(1 mark)

(c) The melting points of aluminium and chlorine are 660 °C and −102 °C respectively.
Explain the difference in the melting points of these two substances in terms of their structure and bonding.

....

....

....

....
(4 marks)

(d) In a reaction, 2.00 kg of aluminium is heated with excess chlorine. 7.14 kg of aluminium chloride is formed.
Calculate the percentage yield of this reaction.
Give your answer to an appropriate number of significant figures.

percentage yield = ... %
(3 marks)

Above a certain temperature, gaseous aluminium chloride forms an equilibrium mixture of $AlCl_3$ and Al_2Cl_6:

$$2AlCl_3 \rightleftharpoons Al_2Cl_6$$

(e) Write an expression for the equilibrium constant, K_c, for this reaction.

....
(1 mark)

(f) Al_2Cl_6 contains two Cl-Al dative covalent bonds, with each Al atom bonded to 4 Cl atoms.
There are no lone pairs around the Al atoms.

(i) Predict the bond angle around each Al atom in Al_2Cl_6.

....
(1 mark)

(ii) Deduce the shape of a molecule of Al_2Cl_6.
Hence draw a 3D diagram showing the bonding and shape of an Al_2Cl_6 molecule.

(2 marks)

EXAM TIP

Being presented with an unfamiliar compound in the exam can be a bit daunting, but don't be alarmed. Try and work out whether it shares any similarities with a compound that you've studied before — you can use this as a guide to predict the properties of the new compound.

Score

[ ]

____

27

Mixed Questions — 2

1   Hex-1-ene and 3-methylpent-2-ene are structural isomers
that belong to the homologous series of alkenes.

(a) (i)   Write the structural formula of 3-methylpent-2-ene.

....

(1 mark)

(ii) 3-methylpent-2-ene exists as a pair of stereoisomers.
Draw the structure of the E isomer of 3-methylpent-2-ene.

(1 mark)

During combustion, hydrocarbons such as hex-1-ene and 3-methylpent-2-ene are oxidised
to produce carbon dioxide and water.

(b) (i)* Describe and explain how the shapes and polarities of carbon dioxide and water molecules determine
their physical states at room temperature (25 °C).

....

....

....

....

....

....

....

....

....

....

....

....

(6 marks)

(ii) Write a balanced symbol equation for the complete combustion of hex-1-ene.

....

(1 mark)

(iii) The enthalpies of combustion of hex-1-ene, carbon and hydrogen are shown in the table below.

Compound	$\Delta_c H$ / kJ mol^{-1}
$H_2C=CH(CH_2)_3CH_{3(l)}$	−4003.4
$C_{(s)}$	−393.5
$H_{2(g)}$	−285.8

Use the data in the table to calculate the enthalpy of formation of hex-1-ene.
The equation for the reaction is: $6C_{(s)} + 6H_{2(g)} \rightarrow H_2C=CH(CH_2)_3CH_{3(l)}$

enthalpy of formation = ... kJ mol^{-1}

(3 marks)

(c) Hex-1-ene reacts readily by electrophilic addition.

(i) Draw a mechanism for the addition reaction of hex-1-ene with hydrogen iodide, HI, to form 2-iodohexane.

(4 marks)

(ii) Hexan-2-ol can be produced by the steam hydration of hex-1-ene.
State a suitable catalyst for this reaction.

....
(1 mark)

(iii) Explain why hexan-2-ol is less volatile than hex-1-ene.

....

....

....
(2 marks)

2 The diagram shows the structure of the alkene chloroethene.

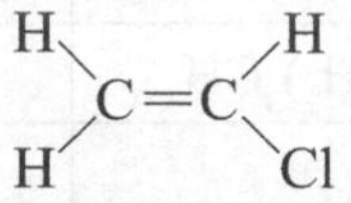

$$\begin{array}{c} H \\ \diagdown \\ H \diagup \end{array} C = C \begin{array}{c} H \\ \diagup \\ \diagdown Cl \end{array}$$

(a) (i) Predict the shape and bond angle around each carbon atom in chloroethene.

Shape:..

Bond angle: ....

(2 marks)

(ii) Explain why chloroethene does **not** exhibit E/Z isomerism.

....

(1 mark)

(b) Describe **one** feature of the double bond in chloroethene that leads to the compound's high reactivity.

....

....

(1 mark)

(c) Chloroethene can undergo an addition polymerisation reaction to form poly(chloroethene) (PVC).

(i) Draw the displayed formula of a section of PVC three repeat units long.

(1 mark)

(ii) One method of disposing of polymers involves burning them to produce energy. Describe **one** problem with disposing of PVC in this way.

....

....

(1 mark)

(d) Chloroethene can also undergo a polymerisation reaction involving chlorine free radicals. The initiation step in this reaction is:

$$Cl_2 \xrightarrow{\text{UV}} 2Cl\cdot$$

The first reaction in the propagation step forms a radical by opening up the C=C double bond. The second results in the formation of a trichlorobutyl radical.

It's fine if you only use molecular formulas here.

(i) Write equations to represent the first two reactions in the propagation step.

....

....

(2 marks)

(ii) Suggest how the amount of chlorine added to the mixture affects the length of the polymer chains in the final product.

....

....

(2 marks)

3 A scientist has a sample of a compound, **X** ($M_r = 88.0$).
The displayed formula of compound **X** is shown below.

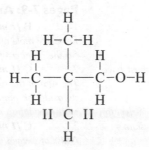

(a) Name compound **X**.

....

(1 mark)

The scientist uses mass spectrometry to analyse a sample of compound **X**.

(b) Explain how the presence of ^{13}C in the sample affects the mass spectrum.

....

....

(1 mark)

(c) The ionisation of molecules during mass spectrometry can cause some of the bonds
within a molecule to break. This produces additional ions which are also detected
by the mass spectrometer. These ions are known as fragment ions.

(i) A peak with m/z = 57 is present in the mass spectrum of compound **X**.
Suggest the displayed formula of the fragment ion that was responsible for this peak.

(1 mark)

(ii) Suggest why the ion you drew in (c)(i) is particularly stable.

....

....

....

(2 marks)

Score

34

Answers

Module 2 — Foundations in Chemistry

Pages 3-6: Atoms, Compounds and Equations

1   C *[1 mark]*
All copper atoms have 29 protons in their nuclei, so copper-64 must have 64 − 29 = 35 neutrons.

2   A *[1 mark]*
Caesium is in Group 1 of the Periodic Table, so it forms 1+ ions. Selenium is in Group 6 of the Periodic Table, so it forms 2− ions. Two caesium ions are needed to balance out the charge on one selenide ion.

3   B *[1 mark]*
To have a charge of +1, the Ag ion must have 1 fewer electrons than protons.

4   B *[1 mark]*
m is the mass of the missing isotope.
$$\frac{(21 \times 0.3) + (20 \times 90.5) + (m \times 9.2)}{100} = 20.187$$
$1816.3 + 9.2m = 2018.7$
$9.2m = 202.4$
$m = 22$

5 a) i)   Isotopes are atoms of the same element with different numbers of neutrons *[1 mark]*.
   ii)   mass number: 17
          atomic number: 8 *[1 mark for both correct]*
   b)   10 *[1 mark]*
   c)   E.g. the model is easy to draw and understand *[1 mark]* and fits well with most observations of e.g. bonding or ionisation energy trends *[1 mark]*.

6 a) i) Na_2SO_4 *[1 mark]*
   ii) $Cu^{2+}_{(aq)} + 2OH^-_{(aq)} \rightarrow Cu(OH)_{2(s)}$ *[1 mark]*
   b) i) $2NaOH + H_2SO_4 \rightarrow Na_2SO_4 + 2H_2O$ *[1 mark]*
   ii) $2Na^+ + 2OH^- + 2H^+ + SO_4^{2-} \rightarrow 2Na^+ + SO_4^{2-} + 2H_2O$
          [1 mark]. $2Na^+$ and SO_4^{2-} are on both sides of the equation so cancel out, giving $2H^+ + 2OH^- \rightarrow 2H_2O$ which can be divided by 2 to give the required equation *[1 mark]*.
If you've shown this visually by crossing through the species which appear on both sides of the equation, rather than explaining in words, you still get the mark.

7 a) $A_r = \frac{(84 \times 0.56) + (86 \times 9.86) + (87 \times 7.02) + (88 \times 82.56)}{100}$
          $= 87.7102$
          $= \textbf{87.7 (1 d.p.)}$
          [2 marks for correct answer given to 1 d.p. or 1 mark for correct method for calculating A_r.]
   b)   Strontium *[1 mark]*

8 a) $2CO + 2NO \rightarrow N_2 + 2CO_2$ *[2 marks — 1 mark for correctly identifying carbon dioxide and 1 mark for a correctly balanced symbol equation]*
   b) $M_r = (3 \times 12.0) + (6 \times 1.0) + (2 \times 16.0)$
          $= 74.0$ *[1 mark]*
   c) i) $4NH_3 + 5O_2 \rightarrow 4NO + 6H_2O$ *[1 mark]*
             $3Cu + 8HNO_3 \rightarrow 3Cu(NO_3)_2 + 2NO + 4H_2O$ *[1 mark]*
   ii)   copper(II) nitrate *[1 mark]*
   iii) Cu^{2+} and NO_3^- *[1 mark for both correct]*
Multiples of any of the balanced equations in question 8 are also correct answers.

9 a)   The weighted mean mass of an atom of an element *[1 mark]* compared to $1/12^{th}$ of the mass of an atom of carbon-12 *[1 mark]*.
   b)   Isotopic mass is the exact mass of an atom of a particular isotope, and not a mean value like relative atomic mass *[1 mark]*.
   c) $M_r = 63.5 + 4(14.0 + (3 \times 1.0)) + 2((2 \times 1.0) + 16.0))$
          $= \textbf{167.5}$ *[1 mark]*
   d) Cl_2 ($M_r = 71.0$) *[1 mark]* and $MnCl_2$ ($M_r = 125.9$) *[1 mark]*

Pages 7-9: Amount of Substance, Acids and Redox — 1

1   B *[1 mark]*
For every mole of PCl_5 molecules, there are 5 moles of Cl atoms. So the number of chlorine atoms is $5 \times 6.02 \times 10^{23} = 3.01 \times 10^{24}$.

2   C *[1 mark]*
The sum of the oxidation numbers in $VOSO_4$ is zero. The sulfate ion has an oxidation number of −2 and the oxygen has an oxidation number of −2, so the oxidation number of vanadium is $0 - (-2) - (-2) = +4$

3   C *[1 mark]*
Mass of oxygen in oxide = 4.26 − 1.86 = 2.40 g.
Moles of P in oxide = 1.86 ÷ 31.0 = 0.06 moles
Moles of O in oxide = 2.40 ÷ 16.0 = 0.15 moles.
Now find the simplest whole number ratio of moles:
0.06 ÷ 0.06 = 1 and 0.15 ÷ 0.06 = 2.5.
Ratio of P to O atoms = 1:2.5 = 2:5. So the empirical formula is P_2O_5.

4   C *[1 mark]*
The number of moles of $BaSO_4$ is 3.16 ÷ 233.4 = 0.0135 moles. The balanced equation shows that one mole of $CuSO_4$ reacts to form one mole of $BaSO_4$. So you need 0.0135 ÷ 0.650 = 0.0208 dm^3 = 20.8 cm^3 of $CuSO_4$ solution to form 3.16 g of $BaSO_4$.

5 a)   Divide by the A_r of each element:
          C: 40.9 ÷ 12.0 = 3.4083...
          H: 4.5 ÷ 1.0 = 4.5
          O: 54.6 ÷ 16.0 = 3.4125
          Divide through by the smallest number:
          C: 3.4083... ÷ 3.4083... = 1.00
          H: 4.5 ÷ 3.4083... = 1.32...
          O: 3.4125 ÷ 3.4083... = 1.00...
          Simplest whole-number ratio of C:H:O = 3:4:3
          Empirical formula = $\textbf{C}_3\textbf{H}_4\textbf{O}_3$
          [2 marks for correct answer, otherwise 1 mark for dividing by the A_r of each element.]
   b)   Empirical mass = $(3 \times 12.0) + (4 \times 1.0) + (3 \times 16.0) = 88.0$
          Number of empirical units = 176.0 ÷ 88.0 = 2
          Molecular formula = $2 \times (C_3H_4O_3) = \textbf{C}_6\textbf{H}_8\textbf{O}_6$ *[1 mark]*
   c)   Mass of ascorbic acid in grams = 300 ÷ 1000 = 0.300 g
          Moles of ascorbic acid = 0.300 ÷ 176.0 = 0.0017045...
          $= \textbf{0.00170 (3 s.f.)}$ *[1 mark]*
You could also give your answer in standard form i.e. 1.70×10^{-3} moles.

6 a)   volume of acid *[1 mark]*
   b) i)

	Titre			
	Rough	1	2	3
Initial reading / cm^3	11.10	28.50	11.25	27.60
Final reading / cm^3	28.50	45.15	27.60	44.30
Volume of HCl added / cm^3	17.40	16.65	16.35	16.70

[2 marks for all four answers correct to 4 significant figures, otherwise 1 mark for three answers correct to 4 significant figures.]
   ii)   mean titre = (16.65 + 16.70) ÷ 2 = 16.675
          $= \textbf{16.68 cm}^3$ **(4 s.f.)**
          [2 marks for correct answer, otherwise 1 mark for including only concordant results in the calculation.]
Concordant results are ones that are very similar to each other (usually within 0.10 cm^3). The result for titre 2 is not concordant with titres 1 and 3, so it shouldn't be included when calculating the mean titre.

iii) Moles of HCl = $0.100 \times 0.016675 = 1.6675 \times 10^{-3}$ mol
The equation shows that there are 2 moles of HCl for each mole of $Ca(OH)_2$.
Moles of $Ca(OH)_2$ in 25 cm³ of diluted solution
$= 1.6675 \times 10^{-3} \div 2 = 8.3375 \times 10^{-4}$ mol
Moles of $Ca(OH)_2$ in original sample
$= (8.3375 \times 10^{-4} \div 25.0) \times 250 = 8.3375 \times 10^{-3}$ mol
Concentration of $Ca(OH)_2 = 8.3375 \times 10^{-3} \div 0.0250$
$= 0.3335$
$= \textbf{0.334 mol dm}^{-3}$ **(3 s.f.)**
[4 marks for correct answer, otherwise 1 mark for correct number of moles of HCl, 1 mark for correct number of moles of $Ca(OH)_2$ in 25 cm³ of diluted solution, 1 mark for correct number of moles of $Ca(OH)_2$ in original sample. Allow error in mean titre value carried forward from question 6 b)ii) throughout.]
Be careful with units in calculations like this. The volumes you're given are in cm³, but the concentrations are in mol dm⁻³. So you need to convert the volume of the $Ca(OH)_2$ solution to dm³ before calculating its concentration. (That's why you divide by 0.0250 in the last step rather than by 25.0.)

7 a) $p = (nRT) \div V$
$= ((2.50 \div 58.0) \times 8.314 \times (10.0 + 273)) \div (750 \times 10^{-6})$
$= 135221.954$ Pa $= 135.22...$ kPa $= \textbf{135 kPa (3 s.f.)}$
[4 marks for correct answer, otherwise 1 mark for correctly working out moles of C_4H_{10}, 1 mark for correctly rearranging the ideal gas equation, 1 mark for substituting correct values into the equation.]
Again, be careful with units here. For the ideal gas equation, volume must be in m³, so in the first step you need to divide by 750×10^{-6} m³ rather than 750 cm³. Temperature must be in K, so you need to add 273 on to the given value of 10 °C. And your answer for pressure will be in Pa, so you'll need to divide it by 1000 to convert it to kPa.

b) Moles of $O_2 = 3.84 \div (2 \times 16.0) = 0.120$
Moles of $C_4H_{10} = 0.120 \div 6.5 = 0.0184...$
Mass of $C_4H_{10} = 0.0184... \times 58.0 = 1.070... = \textbf{1.07 g (3 s.f.)}$
[3 marks for correct answer, otherwise 1 mark for correct number of moles of O_2, 1 mark for correct number of moles of C_4H_{10}.]

Pages 10-13: Amount of Substance, Acids and Redox — 2

1 a) Any two from: e.g. rinse the weighing boat into the flask after transferring the solid/re-weigh the weighing boat after transferring the solid to determine the precise mass of solid added to the flask. / Dissolve the solid in a beaker of water before transferring to the volumetric flask. / Use a funnel to add the solid/solution to the volumetric flask. / Use a pipette to add the last few drops of distilled water to the volumetric flask.
[2 marks — 1 mark for each correct answer.]

b) i) E.g. moles of $NaHCO_3 = 0.30 \times (250 \div 1000) = 0.075$
$M_r(NaHCO_3) = 23.0 + 1.0 + 12.0 + (3 \times 16.0) = 84.0$
Mass of $NaHCO_3 = 0.075 \times 84.0 = \textbf{6.3 g}$
[2 marks for correct answer, otherwise 1 mark for correct working.]
You could also have worked this out by finding the mass of $NaHCO_3$ required to make 1 dm³ of 0.30 mol dm⁻³ solution, and dividing it by 4 to find the mass needed to make 250 cm³ of the solution.

ii) E.g. moles of $NaHCO_3$ in 100 cm³ $= 0.075 \times (100 \div 250)$
$= 0.030$
Concentration of $NaHCO_3 = 0.030 \div (250 \div 1000)$
$= \textbf{0.12 mol dm}^{-3}$
[2 marks for correct answer, otherwise 1 mark for correct number of moles of $NaHCO_3$.]
Another way of finding the number of moles of $NaHCO_3$ in 100 cm³ would be by multiplying the concentration of the standard solution by the volume of the portion removed (100 cm³ ÷ 1000 = 0.1 dm³).

c) Error 1 would decrease the mean titre volume, as the concentration of the standard solution would be higher than intended, meaning less would be needed to neutralise the hydrochloric acid. *[1 mark]*. Error 2 would increase the mean titre volume, as the concentration of the standard solution would be lower than intended, meaning more would be needed to neutralise the hydrochloric acid *[1 mark]*.

2 a) i) Moles of PbS $= (4.50 \times 10^6) \div 239.3 = 18804.84...$ mol
Moles of $O_2 = 18804.84... \times (3 \div 2) = 28207.27...$ mol
Mass of $O_2 = 28207.27... \times (2 \times 16.0) = 902632.67...$ g
$= 902.632...$ kg $= \textbf{903 kg (3 s.f.)}$
[3 marks for correct answer, otherwise 1 mark for correct number of moles of PbS and 1 mark for correct number of moles of O_2.]

ii) E.g. 2 moles of PbS react to give 2 moles of PbO in step 1.
2 moles of PbO reacts to give 2 moles of Pb in step 2.
So 2 moles of PbS reacts to give 2 moles of Pb.
Moles of Pb $= 18804.84...$ mol
Mass of Pb $= 207.2 \times 18804.84... = 3896364.39...$ g
$= 3896.364...$ kg $= \textbf{3900 kg (3 s.f.)}$
[2 marks for correct answer, otherwise 1 mark for correct working.]
You could also have worked this out by finding the mass of lead in 4.5 tonnes of PbS: $(4.50 \times 10^6) \times (207.2 \div 239.3) = 3896364.39...$ g.

b) Atom economy of reaction A $= (A_r(Ti) \div M_r(reactants)) \times 100$
$= 47.9 \div ((47.9 + (4 \times 35.5)) + (2 \times 24.3)) \times 100$
$= \textbf{20.1\% (3 s.f.)}$
Atom economy of reaction B $= (A_r(Ti) \div M_r(reactants)) \times 100$
$= 47.9 \div ((47.9 + (4 \times 35.5)) + (4 \times 23.0)) \times 100$
$= \textbf{17.0\% (3 s.f.)}$
[2 marks — 1 mark for each correct atom economy.]
When you're calculating atom economy, you can divide the molecular mass of the desired product by the total molecular mass of all the reactants or all the products — they'll both be the same.

c) i) MnO_2 *[1 mark]*
ii) iron(III) oxide *[1 mark]*

3 a) i) The copper has been oxidised *[1 mark]*. Its oxidation number has increased from 0 to +2 *[1 mark]*. At the same time, the nitrogen has been reduced *[1 mark]*. Its oxidation number has decreased from +5 to +2 *[1 mark]*.

ii) When a species is reduced, it gains electrons (from another species) *[1 mark]*.

b) i) E.g. moles of Cu = $3.60 \div 63.5 = 0.0566...$ mol
2 moles of Cu are produced from 1 mole of Cu_2S,
so moles of Cu_2S that reacted = $0.0566... \div 2 = 0.0283...$ mol.
The percentage yield of the reaction was 92.4%, so:
Total moles of Cu_2S in sample = $0.0283... \times (100 \div 92.4)$
$= 0.0306...$

Mass of Cu_2S sample = $0.0306... \times ((2 \times 63.5) + 32.1)$
$= 4.8808... = \textbf{4.88 g}$
[4 marks for correct answer, otherwise 1 mark for correct number of moles of Cu, 1 mark for correct number of moles of Cu_2S that reacted, 1 mark for correct total number of moles of Cu_2S in the sample.]

You could also work this out by finding the theoretical mass of Cu that would have formed had all of the Cu_2S reacted, converting the mass to moles, and then using that figure to find the moles and mass of Cu_2S in the sample.

ii) Atom economy = $(M_r(2Cu) \div M_r(reactants)) \times 100$
$= [(2 \times 63.5) \div (((2 \times 63.5) + 32.1) + (2 \times 16.0))] \times 100$
$= \textbf{66.5\% (3 s.f.)}$ *[1 mark]*

Again, it's fine if you divided by the total molecular mass of the products rather than the reactants to reach your answer here.

iii) E.g. reactions with high atom economies produce less waste so are less polluting *[1 mark]*. Reactions with high atom economies make more efficient use of raw materials so are more sustainable *[1 mark]*.

You could also have written your answer in terms of why reactions with low atom economies are less sustainable.

4 a) i) $V = (nRT) \div p$
$= (0.0820 \times 8.314 \times 298) \div (101 \times 10^3)$
$= 2.011... \times 10^{-3}$ m^3
$= 2.01...$ dm$^3 = \textbf{2.01 dm}^3$ **(3 s.f.)**
[3 marks for correct answer, otherwise 1 mark for correctly rearranging the ideal gas equation, 1 mark for substituting correct values into the equation.]

ii) $0.0820 \times 6.02 \times 10^{23} = 4.9364 \times 10^{22}$
$= \textbf{4.94} \times \textbf{10}^{22}$ **(3 s.f.)** *[1 mark]*

b) Percentage of oxygen = $100 - (40.0 + 14.3) = 45.7\%$
In 100 g of the compound, there would be:
$40.0 \div 14.0 = 2.85...$ moles of N
$14.3 \div 1.0 = 14.3$ moles of H
$45.7 \div 16.0 = 2.85...$ moles of O
Divide through by the smallest number:
N: $2.85... \div 2.85... = 1.00$
H: $14.3 \div 2.85... = 5.00$ (3 s.f.)
O: $2.85... \div 2.85... = 1.00$ (3 s.f.)
Empirical formula = NH_5O
[3 marks — 1 mark for correct percentage of oxygen, 1 mark for dividing by the A_r of each element, 1 mark for dividing through by the smallest number of moles.]

c) i) $NH_3 + H_2O \rightarrow NH_4^+ + OH^-$ *[1 mark]*
ii) NH_4NO_3 *[1 mark]*

Pages 14-16: Amount of Substance, Acids and Redox — 3

1 a) $HClO \rightleftharpoons H^+ + ClO^-$ *[1 mark]*
Since this question specifically asks for 'the dissociation reaction', you still get a mark if you used an ordinary arrow instead of the reversible reaction sign.
b) $+1$ *[1 mark]*
c) i) Alkalis are bases that are soluble in water *[1 mark]* and release OH^- ions in aqueous solution *[1 mark]*.
ii) sodium chlorate(I) *[1 mark]*
The ClO^- ion contains oxygen, so it must be a chlorate. You get the (I) from the oxidation state of the chlorine: the overall oxidation state of ClO^- is -1, and the oxygen has an oxidation state of -2, so the chlorine must have an oxidation state of $+1$.
iii) $H^+_{(aq)} + OH^-_{(aq)} \rightarrow H_2O_{(l)}$ *[1 mark]*

2 a) Containing water of crystallisation within the crystal structure *[1 mark]*.
b) Result: mass of crucible/32.2 g *[1 mark]*
Explanation: this result has not been recorded to 2 decimal places *[1 mark]*.
c) i) mass of water = $34.64 - 34.28 = \textbf{0.36 g}$ *[1 mark]*
ii) E.g. the student could have heated the crucible until its mass remained constant *[1 mark]*.
d) Mass of $BaCl_2 = 34.28 - 32.2 = 2.08$ g
Molar mass of $BaCl_2 = 137.3 + (2 \times 35.5) = 208.3$ g mol^{-1}
Moles of $BaCl_2 = 2.08 \div 208.3 = 0.00999... \approx 0.01$
Molar mass of $H_2O = (2 \times 1.0) + 16.0 = 18.0$ g mol^{-1}
Moles of $H_2O = 0.36 \div 18.0 = 0.02$
Ratio of $BaCl_2$ to $H_2O = 0.01 : 0.02 = 1 : 2$, therefore $n = 2$
[3 marks for correct answer, otherwise 1 mark for calculating moles of $BaCl_2$ and 1 mark for calculating moles of H_2O.]
e) n would be too high, as the calculated mass of water would include the mass of the lost crystals/there would be too few moles of $BaCl_2$ in the sample after heating *[1 mark]*.

3 a) Moles of $H_2 = 138 \div 24\,000 = 0.00575$
From the reaction equation the ratio of metal X to H_2 is 1:1, therefore moles of metal X = 0.00575
Molar mass of metal X = 0.14 g $\div$ 0.00575 mol
$= 24.3$ g mol^{-1} (3 s.f.)
metal X = magnesium/Mg
[3 marks — 1 mark for calculating moles of H_2, 1 mark for calculating molar mass of metal X, 1 mark for identifying metal X as magnesium.]
b) $n = (pV) \div (RT)$
$= ((101 \times 10^3) \times (28.9 \times 10^{-6})) \div (8.314 \times 293)$
$= 1.19... \times 10^{-3}$ moles of H_2 produced
1 mole of H_2 is produced from 1 mole of Y, so moles of Y = $1.19... \times 10^{-3}$ mol.
Molar mass of metal Y = mass $\div$ moles
$= 0.0784 \div (1.19... \times 10^{-3}) = 65.4$ g mol^{-1} (3 s.f.)
metal Y = zinc/Zn
[4 marks — 1 mark for correctly rearranging the ideal gas equation, 1 mark for correct number of moles of H_2, 1 mark for calculating molar mass of metal Y, 1 mark for identifying metal Y as zinc.]
c) Source of error: gas escaping once the metal has been added before the bung is replaced *[1 mark]*.
Improvement: e.g. put the metal in a vial in the acid, replace the bung and tip the flask to mix the acid and the metal.
[1 mark for any sensible suggestion.]
d) Moles of Li = $0.0245 \div 6.9 = 3.550... \times 10^{-3}$
From the reaction equation the ratio of Li to H_2 is 2:1,
Therefore moles of $H_2 = (3.550... \times 10^{-3}) \div 2$
$= 1.775... \times 10^{-3}$
Volume of $H_2 = (1.775... \times 10^{-3}) \times 24\,000 = 42.608...$
$= \textbf{42.6 cm}^3$ **(3 s.f.)**
[3 marks for correct answer, otherwise 1 mark for calculating moles of Li, 1 mark for deducing moles of H_2.]
You could also have calculated the volume of H_2 in dm^3 first and then converted to cm^3.

Pages 17-19: Amount of Substance, Acids and Redox — 4

1 a) How to grade your answer:

Level 0: There is no relevant information. *[No marks]*

Level 1: One section is covered well OR two sections are covered but they are incomplete and not always accurate. The answer is not in a logical order. *[1 to 2 marks]*

Level 2: Two sections are covered well OR all 3 sections are covered but they are incomplete and not always accurate. The answer is mostly in a logical order. *[3 to 4 marks]*

Level 3: All 3 sections are covered and are complete and accurate. The answer is coherent and is in a logical order. *[5 to 6 marks]*

Indicative scientific content may include:

Carrying out a titration

Use a pipette to add a set volume of one of the acids to a conical flask.

Add a few drops of an appropriate indicator to the flask.

Fill a burette with the standard solution of sodium hydroxide.

Do a rough titration to get an idea where the end point is.

Add the alkali to the acid using a burette, giving the flask a regular swirl.

Then do an accurate titration. Run the alkali in to within 2 cm³ of the end point. When you get to this stage, add it dropwise.

Repeat the titration several times.

Repeat these steps for the other acid.

Collecting and processing results

Work out the amount of alkali used to neutralise the acid in each accurate titration by subtracting the initial burette reading from the final reading.

Use the results from each repeat to calculate the mean volume of alkali required to neutralise each acid.

Leave out any anomalous results when calculating the mean.

Identifying the acids

The equations for the two reactions are:

$H_2SO_4 + 2NaOH \rightarrow Na_2SO_4 + 2H_2O$

$HCl + NaOH \rightarrow NaCl + H_2O$

H_2SO_4 reacts with NaOH in a 1:2 molar ratio and HCl reacts with NaOH in a 1:1 molar ratio.

So, the acid that required twice as much NaOH to neutralise it is H_2SO_4.

b) i) Oxidation is the loss of electrons *[1 mark]*.

ii) Magnesium has been oxidised, as its oxidation number has increased from 0 to +2 *[1 mark]*.

iii) Effervescence/bubbles of gas *[1 mark]* and the magnesium metal decreasing in size/disappearing *[1 mark]*.

2 a) $n = (pV) \div (RT)$

$= ((101 \times 10^3) \times (280 \times 10^{-6})) \div (8.314 \times (22 + 273))$

$= 0.0115...$ mol of CO_2 produced

1 mole of CO_2 is produced from 1 mole of $CaCO_3$,

so moles of $CaCO_3 = 0.0115...$ mol

Mass of $CaCO_3 = 0.0115... \times (40.1 + 12 + (3 \times 16.0))$

$= 1.15...$ g

Percentage of $CaCO_3$ in sample $= (1.15... \div 1.75) \times 100$

$= 65.954...$

$= \mathbf{66.0\%}$ **(3 s.f.)**

[5 marks for correct answer, otherwise 1 mark for correctly rearranging the ideal gas equation, 1 mark for correct number of moles of CO_2, 1 mark for correct number of moles of $CaCO_3$, 1 mark for correct mass of $CaCO_3$.]

b) i) An acid which only partially dissociates in solution *[1 mark]*.

ii) $2CH_3COOH + CaCO_3 \rightarrow Ca(CH_3COO)_2 + CO_2 + H_2O$ *[1 mark]*

iii) HCl is a strong acid *[1 mark]*, so releases more H^+ ions per mole in solution/has a higher concentration of H^+ ions in the same volume of acid *[1 mark]*.

c) i) $2HCl + CaO \rightarrow CaCl_2 + H_2O$ *[1 mark]*

ii) acid-base/neutralisation *[1 mark]*

iii) This reaction is not a redox reaction, as no element undergoes a change in oxidation number *[1 mark]*.

3 a) Water of crystallisation is the water incorporated into the lattice of a hydrated salt crystal *[1 mark]*.

b) Divide by the A_r of each element:

Mn: $0.668 \div 54.9 = 0.01216...$

Cl: $0.861 \div 35.5 = 0.02425...$

H: $0.097 \div 1.0 = 0.097$

O: $0.776 \div 16.0 = 0.0485$

Divide through by the smallest number:

Mn: $0.01216... \div 0.01216... = 1$

Cl: $0.02425... \div 0.01216... = 1.993...$

H: $0.097 \div 0.01216... = 7.972...$

O: $0.0485 \div 0.01216... = 3.986...$

Simplest whole-number ratio of Mn:Cl:H:O = 1:2:8:4

An 8:4 ratio of H to O indicates that there are 4 molecules of water in the formula.

Formula of compound C = $MnCl_2.4H_2O$

[3 marks for correct answer, otherwise 1 mark for dividing through by the A_r of each element, 1 mark for finding the whole number ratio.]

Pages 20-23: Electrons, Bonding and Structure — 1

1   C *[1 mark]*

Remember, the 4s orbital fills before the 3d orbital to produce the lowest energy arrangement of electrons.

2   D *[1 mark]*

*F_2 doesn't contain any polar bonds, but CBr_4, CO_2 and PF_3 all do.
In CBr_4 and CO_2, the polar bonds are arranged symmetrically:*

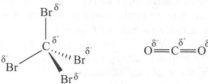

*So neither CBr_4 nor CO_2 has an overall dipole.
But in PF_3 (which is trigonal pyramidal), thanks to the polar bonds, the bottom of the molecule is slightly negative and the top is slightly positive:*

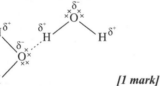   *So PF_3 does have an overall dipole.*

3   C *[1 mark]*

NCl_3 has 3 bonding electron pairs around the central nitrogen atom, and one lone pair — so it must be pyramidal.

4   C *[1 mark]*

5   B *[1 mark]*

Remember, for negative ions you need to add electrons to the atomic electron configuration, and for positive ions you need to take them away.

6 a)   (giant) ionic (lattice) *[1 mark]*

The key idea here is that it's ionic — if you said that, you get the mark.

b)   It takes a lot of energy to overcome the strong electrostatic attractions between the positive and negative ions *[1 mark]*.

c)   Melting or dissolving the substance allows the ions to move and carry a charge *[1 mark]*.

7 a)   E.g.

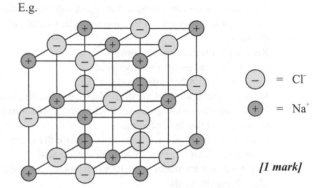

[1 mark]

Oxygen is very electronegative, and so the O–H bonds in water molecules are highly polarised *[1 mark]*, with the O atom having a partial negative charge and the H atoms having partial positive charges *[1 mark]*. Attraction between an H atom from one molecule and a lone pair of electrons on the O atom of another molecule produces a hydrogen bond *[1 mark]*.

You still get the mark for partial charges if you've just labelled them on your diagram and not mentioned them in your explanation.

b)   E.g. the molecules gain enough energy to overcome some of the hydrogen bonds holding them in place in the ice crystal *[1 mark]*.

c)   When liquid water freezes into ice, the number of hydrogen bonds between the molecules increases, producing a regular lattice structure *[1 mark]*. This regular structure holds the molecules further apart on average than the molecules in water/creates empty spaces between the molecules, making ice less dense than water *[1 mark]*.

8 a)   An ionic bond is an electrostatic attraction between a positive ion and a negative ion/two oppositely charged ions *[1 mark]*.

b)   E.g.

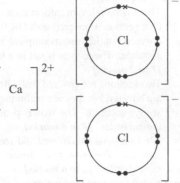

[3 marks — 1 mark for showing Ca^{2+} ion correctly with no (or eight) electrons, 1 mark for showing Cl^- ion correctly with eight electrons, one of which is represented by a different symbol, 1 mark for indicating that there are 2 Cl^- ions]

You could just draw one Cl^- ion with a 2 in front of it for the mark, but it's best to draw both Cl^- ions out in full if you've got time.

c) $1s^2\, 2s^2\, 2p^6$ *[1 mark]*

d)   E.g.

In an ionic compound like NaCl, the ions are packed together in a regular structure called a (giant ionic) lattice *[1 mark]*. The oppositely charged ions *[1 mark]* are strongly attracted to one another in all directions *[1 mark]*.

If you described the alternating arrangement of Na^+ and Cl^- ions instead of showing it on the diagram, you'd still get the mark.

e)   There is a large difference in the electronegativities of Na and Cl, meaning bonds between Na and Cl are strongly polarised and so ionic *[1 mark]*. The difference in the electronegativities of H and Cl is much smaller, and so bonds between them are not strongly polarised and are covalent *[1 mark]*.

9   How to grade your answer:

Level 0:   There is no relevant information. *[No marks]*

Level 1:   There is a good explanation of why one of the molecules given has the observed polarity, or an incomplete explanation of why two of the molecules given have the observed polarities. *[1 to 2 marks]*

Level 2:   There is a good explanation of why two of the molecules given have the observed polarity, or an incomplete explanation of why all three of the molecules given have the observed polarities. *[3 to 4 marks]*

Level 3   There is a complete and accurate explanation of why all three of the molecules given have the observed polarities. The answer is coherent. *[5 to 6 marks]*

Indicative scientific content may include:

Br$_2$

The Br–Br bond in Br_2 is non-polar, as both atoms have the same electronegativity.
So the molecule has no overall dipole.
Diagram to show molecule: Br——Br

CCl₄

All of the C–Cl bonds in CCl₄ are polar, because chlorine is more electronegative than carbon.
But the polar bonds in CCl₄ are arranged symmetrically. This means that the charges cancel out, so the molecule has no permanent dipole and is non-polar.
Diagram to show symmetry:

CHCl₃

All of the C–Cl bonds in CHCl₃ are polar.
Hydrogen is less electronegative than chlorine.
The negative charge is pulled towards the chlorine atoms, making them slightly negative.
So the carbon and hydrogen atoms become slightly positive, creating a permanent dipole.
Diagram to show dipole:

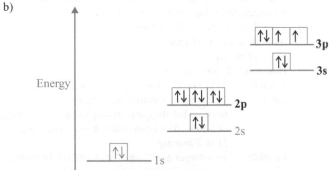

Pages 24-27: Electrons, Bonding and Structure — 2

1 a) i) An atomic orbital is a region around the nucleus that can hold up to two electrons *[1 mark]* with opposite spins *[1 mark]*.

   ii) A: p-orbital
        B: s-orbital
        [1 mark for both correct]

b)

[3 marks — 1 mark for correct 2p, 3s and 3p labels, 1 mark for showing the correct number of electrons in each orbital, 1 mark for showing opposite spins]

c) i) $1s^2\, 2s^2\, 2p^6\, 3s^2\, 3p^6$ *[1 mark]*

   ii) argon *[1 mark]*

2 a) There is a trend of increasing boiling point from H_2S to H_2Te. This is because the induced dipole-dipole interactions/London forces increase as the number of electrons in/size of the Group 6 atoms increases *[1 mark]*.

b) Oxygen is very electronegative, making O–H bonds highly polarised *[1 mark]*, so hydrogen bonds can form between H_2O molecules *[1 mark]*. Hydrogen bonds are stronger than induced dipole-dipole interactions/London forces, so more energy is needed to break them *[1 mark]*.

3 a) i) A dative covalent bond is a covalent bond in which both electrons come from the same atom *[1 mark]*.

   ii)

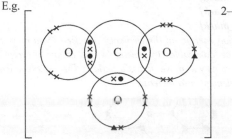

[2 marks — 1 mark for tetrahedral shape represented in 3-D, 1 mark for dative covalent bond shown by arrow]

b) i) The ability of an atom to attract the bonding electrons in a covalent bond *[1 mark]*.

   ii) δ⁺ indicates that the atom has a partial positive charge and δ⁻ indicates that the atom has a partial negative charge *[1 mark]*. So N is more electronegative than H *[1 mark]*.

c) E.g.

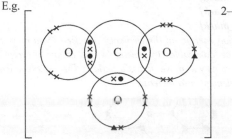

[2 marks — 1 mark for showing bonds correctly, 1 mark for showing other electrons correctly]

You don't need to include the brackets or the charge for the marks here, but it's a good idea to get into the habit of drawing them anyway.

d) E.g. the bonding centres around atoms 2 and 3 all repel each other equally, so are arranged in a tetrahedral shape at an angle of 109.5° to one another *[1 mark]*. This means the central carbon chain is not straight as shown *[1 mark]*, and the bonds in the molecule do not all lie in the same plane *[1 mark]*. The bond angles around carbons 1 and 4 are also shown incorrectly. There are 3 bonding centres and so the bonds are actually at 120° to one another, giving a trigonal planar shape *[1 mark]*.

4 a) i) SF_2:

Diagram with bond angle between 97° and 107° *[1 mark]*.
SF_6:

Shape of SF_2: non-linear *[1 mark]*
Shape of SF_6: octahedral *[1 mark]*

   ii) There are two bonding pairs and two lone pairs around the sulfur atom *[1 mark]*. The electron pairs all repel one another *[1 mark]*, but the lone pairs repel more than the bonding pairs *[1 mark]*, giving SF_2 a non-linear shape.

b) Sulfur is less electronegative than fluorine, so the S–F bond is polar *[1 mark]*. In SF_6, the polar bonds are arranged symmetrically/the charge is evenly distributed across the molecule, so the molecule is non-polar *[1 mark]*. In SF_2, the fluorine atoms pull the shared electrons/negative charge in the same direction *[1 mark]*, creating an uneven distribution of charge across the molecule *[1 mark]*.

c) E.g. SF_2 is a smaller molecule than SF_6, so it will have weaker induced dipole-dipole interactions/London forces *[1 mark]*. But SF_2 also has a permanent dipole (while SF_6 is non-polar), so it will have permanent dipole-dipole interactions *[1 mark]*. Which fluoride has the higher melting point will depend on whether the strength of the SF_2 dipole is greater than the strength of the induced dipole-dipole interactions/London forces in SF_6 *[1 mark]*.

Module 3 — Periodic Table and Energy

Pages 28-30: The Periodic Table — 1

1   B *[1 mark]*
2   D *[1 mark]*
3   B *[1 mark]*
4   C *[1 mark]*

The first ionisation energies of the elements increase as you move down a group in the periodic table. In general (with a couple of exceptions) they also increase as you move across a period. The successive ionisation energies of an element also increase.

5 a) i)   E.g.

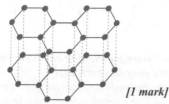

[1 mark]

     The carbon atoms are arranged in sheets of hexagons, with each carbon atom covalently bonded to three other carbon atoms *[1 mark]*. The fourth outer electron of each carbon atom is delocalised *[1 mark]*. The sheets of carbon atoms are held together by induced dipole-dipole/London forces *[1 mark]*.

   ii) E.g. the structure of graphene is the same as that of one of the sheets of carbon atoms in graphite *[1 mark]*.

  b) i) To melt graphite you have to break the strong covalent bonds holding the carbon atoms together *[1 mark]*, which needs a lot of energy *[1 mark]*.

   ii) Electrical conductivity: graphite conducts electricity because it contains delocalised/free electrons *[1 mark]*.
Solubility: graphite is insoluble in any solvent because the covalent bonds between carbon atoms are too strong to be broken by the solvent *[1 mark]*.

  c) Graphene is strong because it consists of a single sheet *[1 mark]* of hexagons, where every carbon atom is joined to three other carbon atoms by strong covalent bonds *[1 mark]*.

6 a) i) $1s^2\ 2s^2\ 2p^6\ 3s^2\ 3p^5$ *[1 mark]*

   ii) $1s^2\ 2s^2\ 2p^6$ *[1 mark]*

  b) i) $Mg + 2HCl \rightarrow MgCl_2 + H_2$ *[1 mark]*

   ii) Magnesium has been oxidised, with its oxidation number increasing from 0 to +2 *[1 mark]*, and hydrogen has been reduced, with its oxidation number decreasing from +1 to 0 *[1 mark]*.

   iii) Strontium has a larger atomic radius *[1 mark]* and more inner shell electrons shielding the outer shell electrons from the nucleus *[1 mark]*. Overall this means the attraction between the nucleus and outer electrons is weaker *[1 mark]*, so it loses electrons more easily *[1 mark]*.

  c) i) E.g. magnesium hydroxide is used as an antacid in some indigestion tablets *[1 mark]*

   ii) The reaction between magnesium and water is very slow. *[1 mark]*

Pages 31-33: The Periodic Table — 2

1 a) The energy needed to remove 1 electron from each atom in 1 mole of gaseous atoms *[1 mark]*.

  b) The overall shape of the graph would be similar *[1 mark]* because of similar sub-shell structure across the periods *[1 mark]*. But the line for Period 2 would be higher *[1 mark]*, because the outer electrons are closer to the nucleus and also less shielded from it, and so take more energy to remove *[1 mark]*.

  c) i) $X^+_{(g)} \rightarrow X^{2+}_{(g)} + e^-$ *[1 mark]*

   ii) The 6th electron is taken from an inner shell/a shell closer to the nucleus *[1 mark]*. It also experiences less shielding by other electrons *[1 mark]*, and so the pull of the nucleus is greater/more energy is required to remove the electron *[1 mark]*.

   iii) nitrogen *[1 mark]*

There is a large difference between the fifth and sixth ionisation energies of element X, which indicates that it has 5 electrons in its outermost shell, and so must be in Group 5 of the Periodic Table. The question tells you it's in Period 2, and so element X can only be nitrogen.

2 a) The strength of the induced dipole-dipole/London forces between molecules of chlorine is weaker than between molecules of iodine *[1 mark]*. This is because the size/mass of the chlorine molecules is less than iodine molecules/chlorine molecules contain fewer electrons than iodine molecules *[1 mark]*.

Chlorine molecules are smaller than iodine molecules because they contain fewer electrons, so have fewer occupied shells and take up less space.

  (b) The reactivity of the halides decreases down the group *[1 mark]*, as the attraction between the nucleus and the outer electrons decreases *[1 mark]*. This is because the halide ions get larger/the electrons are further from the nucleus *[1 mark]*, and because the effect of shielding by the inner electrons increases down the group *[1 mark]*.

  c) i) $Cl_2 + 2Br^- \rightarrow 2Cl^- + Br_2$ *[1 mark]*

   ii) bromide ions/Br$^-$ *[1 mark]*

   iii) white *[1 mark]*

3   How to grade your answer:

Level 0:   There is no relevant information. *[No marks]*

Level 1:   One stage is covered well OR two stages are covered but they are incomplete and not always accurate. The answer is not in a logical order. *[1 to 2 marks]*

Level 2:   Two stages are covered well OR all three stages are covered but they are incomplete and not always accurate. The answer is mostly in a logical order. *[3 to 4 marks]*

Level 3:   All three stages are covered and are complete and accurate. The answer is coherent and is in a logical order. *[5 to 6 marks]*

Indicative scientific content may include:

Stage 1: Metallic substances

Sodium, magnesium and aluminium are metals.

Their melting points increase across the period because the metal-metal bonds get stronger.

The bonds get stronger because the metal ions have an increasing positive charge, an increasing number of delocalised electrons and a decreasing radius.

Stage 2: Silicon

Silicon is giant covalent.

It has a structure made of strong covalent bonds that link all its atoms together.

A lot of energy is needed to break these bonds, so silicon has a high melting point.

Stage 3: Molecular and monoatomic substances

Phosphorus (P_4), sulfur (S_8) and chlorine (Cl_2) are all molecular substances.

Their melting points depend upon the strength of the induced dipole-dipole/London forces between the molecules.

Induced dipole-dipole/London forces are weak and easily overcome so these elements have low melting points.

More atoms in a molecule mean stronger induced dipole-dipole/London forces.

Sulfur forms the biggest molecules, so it's got a higher melting point than phosphorus or chlorine .

Phosphorus is the next biggest, so it has a higher melting point than chlorine

Argon has a very low melting point because it exists as individual atoms (it's monatomic). This results in very weak induced dipole-dipole/London forces.

Pages 34-37: The Periodic Table — 3

1 a) $1s^2\ 2s^2\ 2p^6\ 3s^2\ 3p^6\ 4s^2$ *[1 mark]*

b) The second electron is harder to remove because it is being removed from a positive ion/there are now a greater number of protons than electrons so each outer shell electron receives a greater positive pull from the nucleus *[1 mark]*. There is less repulsion from other electrons so it is held more strongly by the nucleus *[1 mark]*.

c) Jumps between the 2nd and 3rd and the 10th and 11th ionisation energies indicate the presence of discrete shells/energy levels *[1 mark]*, as it takes significantly more energy to remove electrons held in shells/energy levels closer to the nucleus *[1 mark]*. The jump after the 2nd electron is removed indicates two electrons in the outermost shell/energy level *[1 mark]* The jump after the 10th electron is removed indicates 8 electrons in the next shell/energy level *[1 mark]*.

2 a) E.g. the outermost electron of a Group 2 atom is in an s sub-shell *[1 mark]*.

b) i) Group 2 metals become more reactive as you descend the group, because the ionisation energy decreases/the outer electrons are more easily lost as you descend the group *[1 mark]*.

ii) Similarity: e.g. fizzing/bubbles of gas given off *[1 mark]*. Difference: e.g. the reaction of barium would be more vigorous/bubbles of gas would be given off faster *[1 mark]*.

c) i) $CaO_{(s)} + H_2O_{(l)} \rightarrow Ca^{2+}_{(aq)} + 2OH^-_{(aq)}$
[2 marks — 1 mark for correct equation, 1 mark for correct state symbols]

If you've written Ca(OH)$_{2(aq)}$ on the right hand side of the equation that's also correct.

ii) Group 2 metal oxides react with water to produce metal hydroxides *[1 mark]*. Barium hydroxide is more soluble than calcium hydroxide *[1 mark]*, so it will produce more hydroxide ions in solution and have a higher pH than the calcium hydroxide solution *[1 mark]*.

3 a) i) Reaction 2: $Cl_2 + 2NaOH \rightarrow NaClO + NaCl + H_2O$ *[1 mark]*
Reaction 3: $NaClO + H_2O \rightleftharpoons HClO + NaOH$ *[1 mark]*

ii) $Cl_2 + H_2O \rightleftharpoons 2H^+ + Cl^- + ClO^-$ *[1 mark]*

iii) Reactions 1 and 2 *[1 mark]*

b) Any two from: e.g. chlorine gas is very harmful if breathed in. / Liquid chlorine causes severe chemical burns. / Chlorine reacts with organic compounds in water to form chlorinated hydrocarbons. / Chlorine can react to form carcinogenic (cancer-causing) compounds. *[2 marks — 1 mark for each correct answer]*

4 a)

	Experiment 1	Experiment 2	Experiment 3
	$Cl_{2(aq)}$	$Br_{2(aq)}$	$I_{2(aq)}$
KCl$_{(aq)}$		No visible change	No visible change
KBr$_{(aq)}$	Yellow solution forms		No visible change
KI$_{(aq)}$	Orange-brown solution forms	**Orange-brown solution forms**	

[2 marks — 1 mark for each column correct]

(b) Bromine solution/$Br_{2\ (aq)}$ *[1 mark]*

(c) The halogen will dissolve in the cyclohexane *[1 mark]* to form a separate layer above the aqueous solution *[1 mark]*. The yellow aqueous solution will be orange in organic solution *[1 mark]*. The orange-brown solution will be purple in organic solution *[1 mark]*.

(d) equation: $Cl_2 + 2I^- \rightarrow I_2 + 2Cl^-$ *[1 mark]*
oxidising agent: chlorine/Cl_2 *[1 mark]*

(e) No colour change would be seen *[1 mark]*. Bromine is less reactive than fluorine, and so it cannot displace the fluoride ions from solution *[1 mark]*.

There wouldn't be a colour change from a displacement reaction if you mixed bromine solution and sodium fluoride solution — although in reality you might see the colour of the bromine solution lightening, as you're mixing a coloured solution with a colourless one.

5 a) i) The student should have added dilute acid to the test solution before adding the barium chloride solution *[1 mark]*. The acid removes any carbonate or sulfite ions, which would also give a white precipitate with barium chloride *[1 mark]*.

Remember, you can't use sulfuric acid here, because that would add sulfate ions to the solution. So you get the marks if you said acid, or a named acid like hydrochloric or nitric acid, but not if you said sulfuric acid.

ii) Add dilute acid *[1 mark]*. The sodium carbonate solution will effervesce/fizz as carbon dioxide gas is formed *[1 mark]*. The gas collected will turn limewater cloudy *[1 mark]*.

b) Add dilute nitric acid to a sample of the solution *[1 mark]* followed by a few drops of silver nitrate solution *[1 mark]*. A precipitate will form, which will be cream if the solution contains sodium bromide, or yellow if it contains sodium iodide *[1 mark]*. Add concentrated ammonia to the solution *[1 mark]*. A precipitate of silver bromide will dissolve, but a precipitate of silver iodide will not *[1 mark]*.

Pages 38-41: Physical Chemistry — 1

1   A *[1 mark]*

The reaction is exothermic, so decreasing the temperature will favour the forward reaction, and there are more moles of gas on the reactant side than the product side, so increasing the pressure will also favour the forward reaction, leading to an increase in product yield.

2   D *[1 mark]*

Bonds broken: 1 C=C bond, 1 H–Cl bond

Bonds made: 1 C–C bond, 1 C–H bond, 1 C–Cl bond

ΔH = bonds broken − bonds made

    = (612 + 432) − (347 + 413 + 346) = −62 kJ mol⁻¹

3   B *[1 mark]*

500 cm³ of solution has a mass of 500 g, so m = 500 g.

ΔT = 3.5 °C = 3.5 K.

q = mcΔT = 500 g × 4.18 JK⁻¹g⁻¹ × 3.5 K = 7315 J = 7.315 kJ

Moles of NaOH = 0.5 × 0.25 = 0.125 mol

The reaction was exothermic, because the temperature rose. So:

Molar enthalpy change of reaction = $\frac{q}{n}$ = $\frac{-7.315}{0.125}$ = −59 kJ mol⁻¹ (2 s.f.)

4   C *[1 mark]*

5 a)   E.g. An exothermic reaction gives out energy *[1 mark]* and so has negative enthalpy change/negative DH *[1 mark]*.

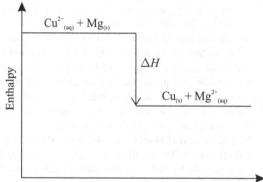

[2 marks — 1 mark for showing reactants with higher enthalpy than products, 1 mark for arrow pointing downwards labelled DH]

If you've just written 'reactants' on your higher energy line and 'products' on your lower energy line you still get the mark.

b) i)   percentage uncertainty = $\frac{\text{uncertainty}}{\text{quantity measured}} \times 100\%$

                    = $\frac{0.1}{20} \times 100\%$ = **0.5% *[1 mark]***

ii)   E.g. the student should make sure that the copper(II) sulfate solution is disposed of correctly/not poured down the drain. / The student should wear gloves to protect their hands *[1 mark for any sensible suggestion]*.

c)   20 cm³ of solution has a mass of 20 g, so *m* = 20 g

     ΔT = 55 °C = 55 K

     $q = mc\Delta T$ = 20 × 4.18 × 55 = 4598 J = 4.598 kJ

     Moles of CuSO₄ = 0.50 × (20 ÷ 1000) = 0.010 mol

     $\Delta_r H = \frac{-4.598}{0.010}$ = −459.8 = **−460 kJ mol⁻¹ (2 s.f.)**

[4 marks for correct answer given to 2 s.f. or 3 marks for correct answer not given to 2 s.f., otherwise 1 mark for correctly substituting the values into q = mcΔT and 1 mark for correct units.]

You still get full marks if you gave a correct answer in J mol⁻¹.

d) i)   E.g. heat was lost from the system to the surroundings *[1 mark]*.

ii)   E.g. insulate the system more/use a polystyrene beaker/put a lid on the beaker *[1 mark]*.

6 a)   A reaction where all of the reactants and products are in the same physical state/phase *[1 mark]*.

b) $K_c = \dfrac{[CH_3OH]}{[CO][H_2]^2}$ *[1 mark]*

c)   There are 3 moles of gas on the reactant side and only 1 mole of gas on the product side *[1 mark]*. Increasing the pressure will shift the equilibrium to the right/towards the products (to lower the pressure again) *[1 mark]*, which will increase the yield of methanol *[1 mark]*.

d) i)   At a higher temperature the molecules have more energy, so more molecules will have enough energy to react/energy above the activation energy *[1 mark]*. At a higher temperature, the molecules move more quickly, so collisions will be more frequent *[1 mark]*.

ii)   The reaction is exothermic, so increasing the temperature would shift the equilibrium to the left/in the endothermic direction (to try to decrease the temperature) *[1 mark]*. This would decrease the yield of methanol *[1 mark]*. Using a catalyst is a better option because it increases the rate of reaction without affecting the position of equilibrium/yield of methanol *[1 mark]*.

(e) $\Delta_r H^\ominus = \Sigma\, \Delta_f H^\ominus$ products − $\Sigma\, \Delta_f H^\ominus$ reactants

     $\Delta_r H^\ominus$ = ((2 × −108.7) + (2 × −285.8)) − ((2 × −239.1) + 0)

           = **−310.8 kJ mol⁻¹**

[2 marks for correct answer, otherwise 1 mark for stating the formula for $\Delta_r H^\ominus$]

It's fine if you drew a Hess's law diagram to work out what calculation you needed to do here, instead of just stating the formula.

Pages 42-44: Physical Chemistry — 2

1 a) i) A homogeneous catalyst is a catalyst which is in the same physical state/phase as the reactants *[1 mark]*.

  ii) The use of catalysts means that lower temperatures and pressures can be used *[1 mark]*. Less energy is needed to create these temperatures and pressures, and so less polluting gases such as CO_2 are produced *[1 mark]*. Catalysts sometimes also allow alternative reactions with fewer steps and better atom economy to be used, creating less waste and preserving resources *[1 mark]*.

 b) i) An increase in the concentration of chloride ions would make the solution bluer in colour *[1 mark]*. This colour change would occur because the position of equilibrium would shift to the right to oppose the change and decrease the concentration of chloride ions *[1 mark]*.

  ii) E.g. decrease the temperature of the equilibrium mixture and examine the colour of the mixture to determine whether the reaction had moved in the forwards or backwards direction *[1 mark]*.

  iii) If the forwards reaction is endothermic, decreasing the temperature will cause the solution to appear pinker in colour *[1 mark]*, as the equilibrium shifts in the exothermic direction to oppose the change *[1 mark]*.

2 a) i) E.g.

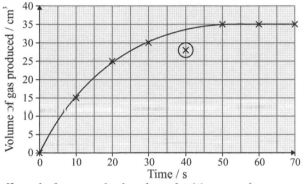

[3 marks for correctly plotted graph with appropriate trend line, otherwise 1 mark for correctly labelled axes and 1 mark for correctly plotted data points.]

  ii) Point circled as on graph above *[1 mark]*.
  E.g. the students might have measured or recorded the volume incorrectly *[1 mark]*.

  iii) E.g.

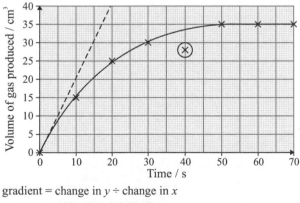

gradient = change in y ÷ change in x

= $(40 - 0) ÷ (19.5 - 0)$

= 2.0512... cm^3 s^{-1}

Rate = 2.1 cm^3 s^{-1} (2 s.f.)
[1 mark for tangent drawn at t = 0 s, 1 mark for calculating rate from gradient of tangent drawn]

  iv) The rate of reaction depends on the frequency of successful collisions between H^+ ions and the surface of the magnesium *[1 mark]*. As the reaction proceeds, the H^+ ions are used up, so successful collisions become less frequent and the rate decreases *[1 mark]*.

b) i) At an increased temperature, a greater proportion of the particles would have at least the activation energy for the reaction and be able to react *[1 mark]*, and so the rate of reaction would increase *[1 mark]*.

  ii) Increasing the concentration of HCl to 2 mol dm^{-3} would increase the number of ions in solution, meaning that collisions between the hydrogen ions and the magnesium became more frequent *[1 mark]*. More collisions in total means more successful collisions, and so the initial rate of reaction would be higher *[1 mark]*.

c) i) E.g. use a gas syringe/collect the gas over water in an upturned measuring cylinder *[1 mark]*.

  ii) Any two from: e.g. the apparatus must not let any gas escape. / The apparatus must be large enough to collect all the gas produced. / The apparatus needs to have the right level of sensitivity. *[2 marks — 1 mark for each sensible factor.]*

Pages 45-47: Physical Chemistry — 3

1 a) i) Bonds broken: 2 C–C bonds, 8 C–H bonds, 5 O=O bonds

Energy absorbed = $(2 \times 347) + (8 \times 413) + (5 \times 498)$
= 6488 kJ mol^{-1}

Bonds made: 6 C=O bonds, 8 O–H bonds
Energy released = $(6 \times 805) + (8 \times 464)$
= 8542 kJ mol^{-1}

Enthalpy of reaction = energy absorbed – energy released
= 6488 – 8542 = **–2054 kJ mol^{-1}**

[3 marks for correct answer, otherwise 1 mark for calculating enthalpy of bonds broken and 1 mark for calculating enthalpy of bonds made.]

ii) $\Delta_c H = \Sigma \Delta_f H$ products – $\Sigma \Delta_f H$ reactants
= $((3 \times -393.5) + (4 \times -241.8)) - (-104.5)$
= $-2147.7 + 104.5 =$ **–2043.2 kJ mol^{-1}**

[3 marks for correct answer, otherwise 1 mark for stating the formula and 1 mark for correctly substituting the enthalpies of formation into the formula.]

Again, you still get the mark if you drew a Hess's law diagram here, instead of just stating the formula.

iii) Mean bond enthalpies are average values over a range of compounds *[1 mark]*. The enthalpies of formation given are for the exact compounds in this reaction *[1 mark]*.

b) 50.0 cm^3 of water has a mass of 50.0 g, so m = 50.0 g
ΔT = 74.0 °C – 21.5 °C = 52.5 °C = 52.5 K
$q = mc\Delta T$ = $50.0 \times 4.18 \times 52.5$ = 10972.5 J = 10.9725 kJ
Mass of propan-2-ol burned = 75.2 – 74.8 = 0.4 g
M_r of propan-2-ol = $(12.0 \times 3) + (16.0 \times 1) + (1.0 \times 8)$
= 60.0 g mol^{-1}

moles of propan-2-ol burnt = $\dfrac{0.4}{60.0}$ = 0.00666... mol

$\Delta_c H = \dfrac{-10.9725}{0.00666...}$ = -1645.875 = **–1650 kJ mol^{-1} (3 s.f.)**

[5 marks for correct answer, otherwise 1 mark for finding the temperature change, 1 mark for calculating q using $q = mc\Delta T$, 1 mark for finding the mass of propan-2-ol burned and 1 mark for finding the number of moles of propan-2-ol burned.]

2 a) Increasing the pressure will increase the rate of reaction *[1 mark]*. At higher pressure, there will be more oxygen molecules in a given volume/the molecules will be pushed closer together *[1 mark]*, so collisions between the oxygen molecules and the potassium metal are more likely *[1 mark]*. More collisions means more successful collisions and a higher rate of reaction *[1 mark]*.

b) i)

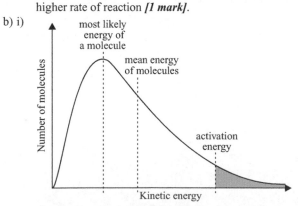

[1 mark for shading correct area.]

ii) Adding a catalyst provides a different reaction route with lower activation energy *[1 mark]*, meaning that a greater number of molecules will have sufficient energy to react *[1 mark]*.

iii)

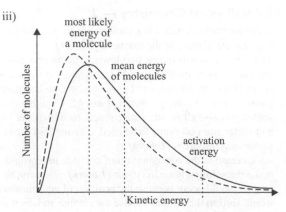

[2 marks — 1 mark for peak to left of existing peak, 1 mark for peak higher than existing peak.]

c) Measure the change in mass over time *[1 mark]*.
Measure the volume of gas given off over time *[1 mark]*.

Pages 48-49: Physical Chemistry — 4

1 a) Any two from: e.g. the forward and reverse reactions must be proceeding at the same rate. / The concentrations of the reactants and products must remain constant / The reaction must take place in a closed system. *[2 marks — 1 mark for each correct condition.]*

b) i) In this reaction, two moles of reactant give four moles of product/there are more moles of products than of reactants *[1 mark]*. Increasing the pressure would shift the equilibrium in favour of the reactants, reducing the yield of acetylene *[1 mark]*.

ii) How to grade your answer:

Level 0: There is no relevant information. *[No marks]*

Level 1: One factor from rate, yield and cost is covered well OR two factors are covered but they are covered incompletely and not always accurately. The answer is not in a logical order. *[1 to 2 marks]*

Level 2: Two factors from rate, yield and cost are covered well OR all three factors are covered but they are covered incompletely and not always accurately. The answer is mostly in a logical order. *[3 to 4 marks]*

Level 3: All three factors are covered completely and accurately. The answer is coherent and is in a logical order. *[5 to 6 marks]*

Indicative content:

Rate of reaction

Using a high temperature will increase the rate of reaction. This is because the particles have more kinetic energy on average, so they will collide more frequently and more of the collisions will be successful

A higher rate of reaction means that the product (acetylene) can be produced more quickly.

Yield (equilibrium position)

The forward reaction is endothermic.

Using a high temperature will shift the equilibrium in favour of the product.

This will increase the yield of acetylene.

Cost

A high temperature is beneficial in terms of yield and rate of reaction.

However, high temperatures require a lot of energy to produce and maintain. This can be expensive.

High temperatures may also require specialised equipment. Therefore a compromise temperature must be chosen that is as high as possible (to give a good rate and yield) without costing too much to produce and maintain.

c) i) $K_c = \dfrac{[H_2]^3[C_2H_2]}{[CH_4]^2}$ *[1 mark]*

ii) From the equation, 1 mole of acetylene is produced from 2 moles of methane, so 0.372 moles of acetylene must be produced from $2 \times 0.372 = 0.744$ moles of methane. Therefore there must be $1.00 - 0.744 = 0.256$ moles of methane left at equilibrium

3 moles of hydrogen are produced for every 1 mole of acetylene so $0.372 \times 3 = 1.116$ moles of hydrogen were present at equilibrium.

Equilibrium concentrations:

$[C_2H_2] = \dfrac{0.372}{3.00} = 0.124$ mol dm^{-3}

$[H_2] = \dfrac{1.116}{3.00} = 0.372$ mol dm^{-3}

$[CH_4] = \dfrac{0.256}{3.00} = 0.0853...$ mol dm^{-3}

$K_c = \dfrac{0.372^3 \times 0.124}{(0.0853...)^2} = 0.8766...$

$K_c = 0.877$ mol^2 dm^{-6} (3 s.f.)

[7 marks for correct answer given to 3 s.f. or 6 marks for correct answer not given to 3 s.f., otherwise 1 mark for number of moles of methane at equilibrium correct, 1 mark for number of moles of hydrogen at equilibrium correct, 1 mark for each equilibrium concentration correct.]

iii) K_c has increased and so the position of equilibrium must have moved towards the products/to the right *[1 mark]*. This means the yield of acetylene will increase *[1 mark]*.

Module 4 — Core Organic Chemistry

Pages 50-53: Basic Concepts and Hydrocarbons — 1

1   C *[1 mark]*

The general formula of the alkanes is C_nH_{2n+2}. So an alkane with 16 H atoms will have 7 C atoms, because $(7 \times 2) + 2 = 16$.

2   A *[1 mark]*

To figure this out, you need to use the Cahn-Ingold-Prelog priority rules. Alkene N has two F atoms attached to the first double bond carbon, so it doesn't have stereoisomers. Of the other three, alkene M is the only one that has the two higher priority groups on the same side of the double bond.

3   B *[1 mark]*

To show stereoisomerism, both of an alkene's double bond carbons must have two different groups attached to them. In 2-methylbut-2-ene, the first double bond carbon has two CH_3 groups attached to it.

4   B *[1 mark]*

The H^+ and Br^- from HBr are added to the carbons either side of where the double bond is in the original molecule.

5 a)   A/B *[1 mark]*

b)

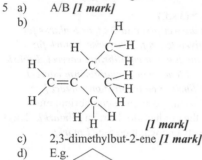

[1 mark]

c)   2,3-dimethylbut-2-ene *[1 mark]*

d)   E.g.

[1 mark]

Any molecule with the formula C_6H_{12} that isn't an alkene is fine here.

6 a)   E.g. saturated organic compounds contain only single bonds between carbon atoms/contain no double or triple bonds between carbon atoms *[1 mark]*.

b)   Any two from: e.g. compounds in a homologous series have similar chemical properties. / Compounds in a homologous series have the same general formula. / Compounds in a homologous series have the same functional group. / Each successive member in a homologous series differs by a CH_2 group. *[2 marks — 1 mark for each correct answer.]*

c) CH_3COOH *[1 mark]*

d)   3,4-dimethylpentanoic acid *[1 mark]*

7 a) i)   22 *[1 mark]*

Don't forget to include all the C–H bonds, even though they're not shown in the skeletal formula, and the σ-bond in the double bond.

ii) C_8H_{14} *[1 mark]*

iii)   A and B are aliphatic compounds that have their carbon atoms arranged in a non-aromatic ring structure *[1 mark]*.

b)   E.g.

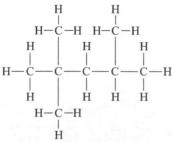

[1 mark for a displayed formula of an aliphatic, branched-chain alkane with 8 carbon atoms.]

c) i)   E.g. $CH_2C(CH_3)CH_2CH_2CH_3$
[1 mark for a structural formula of an alkene with the molecular formula C_6H_{12} and two identical groups bonded to the same C atom in the double bond.]

ii)   Any two from: e.g.

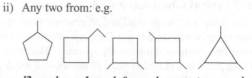

[2 marks — 1 mark for each correct answer.]

iii) $C_6H_{12} + 9O_2 \rightarrow 6CO_2 + 6H_2O$ *[1 mark]*

d) i) $C_nH_{2n+1}Cl$ *[1 mark]*

ii)   C and D *[1 mark]*

Both C and D have 5 carbon atoms, whereas E has 4 and F has 6.

iii)   3-chloropentane *[1 mark]*

Pages 54-57 : Basic Concepts and Hydrocarbons — 2

1 a)

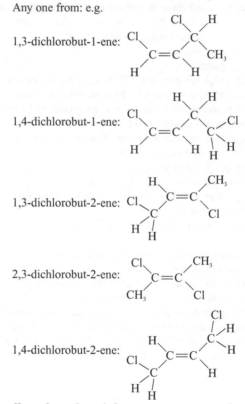

For this one, it doesn't matter if you drew out all the bonds in the $-CH_2CH_3$ group (or if you showed it as C_2H_5). You could also have drawn a skeletal formula.

b)   Both of the double-bond carbons have two different atoms or groups attached to them *[1 mark]* and there is restricted rotation around the double bond *[1 mark]*.

c)   Any one from: e.g.

1,3-dichlorobut-1-ene:

1,4-dichlorobut-1-ene:

1,3-dichlorobut-2-ene:

2,3-dichlorobut-2-ene:

1,4-dichlorobut-2-ene:

[2 marks — 1 mark for a correct structure, 1 mark for a name that matches the structure drawn.]

There are a few more possible answers for this question — you get the marks if you correctly drew and named any isomer of $C_4H_6Cl_2$ that has a double bond with different groups attached to both double-bond carbons.

d)   E.g. 1,1-dichlorobut-1-ene / 2,3-dichlorobut-1-ene / 3,3-dichlorobut-1-ene/ 3,4-dichlorobut-1-ene / 4,4-dichlorobut-1-ene *[1 mark]*.

You'd get a mark here for naming any alkene isomer of $C_4H_6Cl_2$ that has identical atoms or groups attached to either of the double-bond carbons.

2 a)

but-2-ene *[1 mark]*

You'd get the mark for the diagram here if you just wrote 'CH₃' instead of drawing out the two methyl groups in full, or if you drew a skeletal formula.

b) i)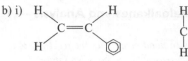

[2 marks — 1 mark for each correct structure.]

ii) A compound that contains a benzene ring [1 mark].

3 a) i) Type of bond: Pi/π-bond [1 mark]
Explanation: This arises by sideways overlap of adjacent p-orbitals above and below the molecular axis/bonding carbon atoms [1 mark].

ii) Bond angle: 120° [1 mark]
Explanation: There are three covalent bonds around the carbon atom which all repel evenly [1 mark].

b) Of the groups attached to the left hand carbon of the C=C, CH₃ takes priority over H, since C has a higher atomic number than H [1 mark]. Both groups attached to the right hand carbon of the C=C contain C atoms, so it is necessary to look further down the chain [1 mark]. The methyl/bottom carbon is only attached to H atoms, but the ethyl/top carbon is attached to another C atom, so the ethyl/top carbon takes priority [1 mark]. The highest priority groups are on the same side of the double bond, so the isomer is Z [1 mark]. The systematic name is therefore Z-3-methylpent-2-ene [1 mark].

c) i) In alkene A, each of the carbon atoms in the double bond has a methyl/CH₃ group attached to it [1 mark].

ii) E.g.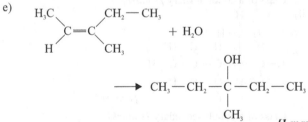

There are a few other possible answers for this question. Remember, an alkene will only show cis/trans isomerism if each carbon atom in the double bond is attached to two different groups, and the carbon atoms have at least one attached group in common. As long as you've drawn the structure of an alkene with the molecular formula C₆H₁₂ that doesn't fit these criteria, you get the mark.

d) i)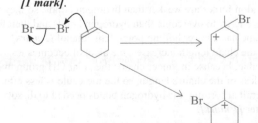

[1 mark]

ii) The pi/π-bond in alkene A has a lower bond enthalpy than the sigma/σ-bonds in the alkane/product. / The electron density of the double bond attracts electrophiles. [1 mark]

e)

[1 mark]
Reactions conditions: steam and an acid catalyst [1 mark]

4 a) The solution would be decolourised/turn from orange to colourless [1 mark].

b) The double bond is a region of high electron density [1 mark].

c)

[1 mark for curly arrow from C=C to bromine atom, 1 mark for curly arrow from Br–Br bond to other bromine atom.]

d) Carbocation B is more likely to be formed, as it is a tertiary carbocation, so it is more stable than A (a secondary carbocation) [1 mark].

e)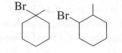

[2 marks — 1 mark for each correct structure]

Pages 58-60 : Basic Concepts and Hydrocarbons — 3

1 a) i) Bond angle: 109.5° [1 mark]
Shape: tetrahedral [1 mark]

ii) [1 mark]

b) How to grade your answer:
Level 0: There is no relevant information. [No marks]
Level 1: The answer covers one factor affecting the boiling points of hydrocarbons and an attempt to place the compounds in order is made. The answer has no clear structure. The information given is basic and lacking in detail. It may not all be relevant or correct. [1 to 2 marks]
Level 2: The answer covers both factors affecting the boiling points of hydrocarbons and the compounds are placed in the correct order. The answer has some structure. Most of the information given is relevant and there is some detail involved. [3 to 4 marks]
Level 3: The answers covers both factors affecting boiling points of hydrocarbons in detail and the compounds are placed in the correct order, including full reasoning. The answer has a clear and logical structure. The information given is relevant and detailed. [5 to 6 marks]

Indicative scientific content may include:
How chain length affects the boiling points of hydrocarbons
Hydrocarbons have covalent bonds between the atoms and induced dipole-dipole interactions/London forces between the molecules.
A larger/longer molecule has a greater number of electrons to interact.
A larger/longer molecule has stronger induced dipole-dipole interactions/London forces.
A larger/longer molecule has a greater surface area of contact.
The more induced dipole-dipole interactions/London forces, the greater the energy required to overcome them and the higher the boiling point.
How branching affects the boiling points of hydrocarbons
Branched-chain hydrocarbons cannot pack together as closely as straight-chain hydrocarbons.
They have a smaller surface area of contact.
So there are fewer induced dipole-dipole interactions/London forces between molecules.
Less energy is required to overcome fewer induced dipole-dipole interactions/London forces, and so the boiling point is lower.
Compounds A-C in order of boiling point
Compound C has the highest boiling point, as it has the longest carbon chain/is the largest molecule, and is not branched.
Compounds A and B contain the same number of carbon atoms, but compound A has a straight chain and compound B has a branched chain, therefore compound A has a higher boiling point than compound B.

c) Compound D is more reactive than compound B. The C–Cl bond has lower enthalpy than the C–H bond, therefore less energy is required to break it *[1 mark]*. There is a larger difference in electronegativity between C and Cl than between C and H, so the C–Cl bond is more polar than the C–H bond *[1 mark]*. This makes the C–Cl bond more open to (nucleophilic) attack *[1 mark]*.

d) i) When bonds break by homolytic fission, each bonded atom receives one electron from the bonded pair *[1 mark]*. Whereas when bonds break by heterolytic fission, one of the bonded atoms receives both electrons from the bonded pair *[1 mark]*.

   ii) $C(CH_3)_3^+$ and Cl^- *[1 mark]*

2 a) i) Initiation: $Cl_2 \xrightarrow{UV} 2Cl\bullet$
Propagation step 1: $Cl\bullet + CH_3CH_3 \rightarrow \bullet CH_2CH_3 + HCl$
Propagation step 2: $\bullet CH_2CH_3 + Cl_2 \rightarrow CH_3CH_2Cl + Cl\bullet$
Propagation step 3: $Cl\bullet + CH_3CH_2Cl \rightarrow \bullet CH_2CH_2Cl + HCl$
Termination: $\bullet CH_2CH_2Cl + Cl\bullet \rightarrow CH_2ClCH_2Cl$
[5 marks — 1 mark for each correct step]

Remember, the total number of radicals doesn't change during a propagation reaction, so if a radical is involved in the reaction, another radical must be formed.

   ii) E.g. the radicals involved in this reaction mechanism can join together in many different ways/be involved in many different termination reactions to produce a range of products (such as C_4H_{10} or C_4H_9Cl) *[1 mark]*. Some of the ethane molecules will only be substituted once by chlorine, whereas others may be substituted 3 or more times *[1 mark]*.

b) i) Any two from: e.g. combustion produces heat energy that can be used to generate electricity. / Combustion reduces the amount of waste sent to landfill. / Smaller areas of land are required for incinerators than for landfill sites.
[2 marks — 1 mark for each correct benefit]

   ii) E.g. the demand for new raw materials to produce polymers and other products is reduced. / Finite resources are conserved by processing waste in this way. / Fewer toxic by-products are produced. *[1 mark]*

c) i) E.g. biodegradable plastics can be made from renewable materials such as starch *[1 mark]*, reducing dependency on finite resources such as crude oil *[1 mark]*. Biodegradable plastics decompose quickly in the natural environment *[1 mark]*, which reduces the amount of persistent plastic waste *[1 mark]*.

   ii) Biodegradable polymers need light and water in order that microorganisms can digest them *[1 mark]*, and photodegradable polymers only break down in the presence of sunlight *[1 mark]*.

Pages 61-64: Alcohols, Haloalkanes and Analysis — 1

1   B *[1 mark]*
The strength of the carbon–halogen bond determines the reactivity of a haloalkane. The bond strength decreases as you go down Group 7 — so the C–I bond breaks most easily, and 1-iodobutane will react faster than 1-chlorobutane or 1-bromobutane.

2   C *[1 mark]*
$NH_2CH_2CH_2NH_2$, $CH_3CH_2CH_2OH$ and CH_3COOH all show up as having an M_r of 60 in a mass spectrometer, whereas CH_3COCH_3 has an M_r of 58.

3   A *[1 mark]*
A is a primary alcohol, so you can oxidise it to an aldehyde. But you can't eliminate an H_2O molecule, because the carbon atom next to the one with the -OH group can't donate an H^+.

4   B *[1 mark]*
$C=O$ bonds cause peaks in the range 1630-1820 cm^{-1}, and O–H bonds in carboxylic acid groups cause broad peaks in the range 2500-3300 cm^{-1}.

5 a) E.g. potassium dichromate(VI) / $K_2Cr_2O_7$ *[1 mark]*

   b) The method shown is distillation *[1 mark]*. The aldehyde has a lower boiling point than the alcohol, so it boils off from the reaction mixture first and can be collected as soon as it is formed *[1 mark]*.

   c) A: a water bath is used to heat the alcohol instead of a naked flame as alcohols are flammable/to heat the reaction mixture more evenly/gently *[1 mark]*.
B: anti-bumping granules are used to give a smooth and even boil / prevent the formation of large bubbles *[1 mark]*.
C: an ice bath is used so that the (volatile) aldehyde does not evaporate *[1 mark]*.

   d) Use reflux apparatus/vertical condenser *[1 mark]*.
The vaporised substances cool and condense and return back to the reaction mixture *[1 mark]*. This ensures that the alcohol is fully oxidised to a carboxylic acid *[1 mark]*.

   e) $CH_3CH_2OH + 2[O] \rightarrow CH_3COOH + H_2O$ *[1 mark]*

6 a) i)

Class of alcohol: tertiary *[1 mark]*

   ii)

Class of alcohol: secondary *[1 mark]*

   b) $C_5H_{11}OH + 7\frac{1}{2}O_2 \rightarrow 5CO_2 + 6H_2O$ *[1 mark]*

   c) i) Ethanol has hydrogen bonding between the molecules *[1 mark]*. Ethane molecules have only induced dipole-dipole interactions/London forces between the molecules *[1 mark]*. Induced dipole-dipole interactions/London forces are weaker than hydrogen bonds, so they take less energy to overcome than hydrogen bonds and therefore ethane has a lower boiling point than ethanol *[1 mark]*.

   ii) As the chain length increases, the alcohol becomes less soluble, because in longer chains the polar OH group makes up less of the chain's length, so the molecule is less effective overall at forming the hydrogen bonds needed to dissolve in water *[1 mark]*.

d)

2-chloro-3-methylbutane *[1 mark]*

7 a) A nucleophile is an electron pair donor *[1 mark]*.

b) i) The OH⁻/hydroxide ion *[1 mark]*

ii)

[3 marks — 1 mark for the curly arrow from the lone pair or negative charge on the OH⁻ ion to the δ+ C atom, 1 mark for the correct δ+ and δ– symbols and correct curly arrow on the C–I bond, 1 mark for showing both products correctly.]

iii) There are no polar bonds in ethane to attract the nucleophile/OH⁻ *[1 mark]*.

c) hexane-2,3-diol *[1 mark]*

Pages 65-67: Alcohols, Haloalkanes and Analysis — 2

1 a) alkene and alcohol *[1 mark]*

b) i) Compound B will undergo an electrophilic addition reaction due to the presence of the C=C bond *[1 mark]*. The bromine water will be decolourised *[1 mark]*.

ii) An oxidation reaction takes place, because compound B contains a primary alcohol group / the alcohol will be oxidised to a carboxylic acid *[1 mark]*. The acidified potassium dichromate(VI) changes colour from orange to green *[1 mark]*.

c) i) Type of reaction: Elimination *[1 mark]*
Reagents and conditions: Concentrated sulfuric/phosphoric acid catalyst, heat *[1 mark]*

ii) Type of reaction: Addition *[1 mark]*
Reagents and conditions: H₂/hydrogen gas *[1 mark]*, nickel catalyst and temperature of 150 °C *[1 mark]*

2 a) E.g. Greenhouse gases contain bonds which absorb and re-emit infrared radiation *[1 mark]*. The peaks shown on the infrared spectrum of a molecule represent the frequencies at which its bonds absorb IR radiation *[1 mark]*. The IR spectra of water, carbon dioxide and methane will contain peaks caused by the O-H, C=O and C-H bonds which allow them to act as greenhouse gases *[1 mark]*.

b) E.g. the alcohol group contains an O-H bond, but this bond will also be present in the water vapour in the driver's breath *[1 mark]*.

c) Compound I is butanal *[1 mark]*. There is a peak at around 1750 cm⁻¹ for the C=O bond, which is only present in butanal *[1 mark]*. There is no peak at 3200-3600 cm⁻¹/1000-1300 cm⁻¹, which would be expected for the O-H/C-O peak if compound I were butanol *[1 mark]*. There is no peak at 1620-1680 cm⁻¹, which would be expected for the C=C bond if compound I were but-2-ene *[1 mark]*.

3 a) Water is a weak nucleophile *[1 mark]*.

b) Going down the group from C-F to C-I, the bond enthalpy decreases so the rate of hydrolysis will increase *[1 mark]*. The lower the bond enthalpy, the weaker the bond and the less time it takes to hydrolyse (break) the bond *[1 mark]*.

c) How to grade your answer:

Level 0: There is no relevant information. *[No marks]*

Level 1: A simple description of the method is given, which may include some errors or omissions.
[1 to 2 marks]

Level 2: Attempts a description of the method including equations and details of how to ensure a fair test, but explanations may be incomplete.
[3 to 4 marks]

Level 3: Gives a comprehensive description of a method that allows the trend in rate to be identified, including full, balanced equations and complete details of how to ensure a fair test.
[5 to 6 marks]

Indicative chemistry content may include:

Carrying out the test

Fill three test tubes with ethanol.
Into the first test tube add a small amount of 1-chlorobutane.
Add a small amount of 1-bromobutane into the second tube and a small amount of 1-iodobutane into the third tube.
Heat the three tubes up in a water bath for several minutes.
Add a small amount of silver nitrate solution to each test tube. Start the stop watch immediately.
Record and compare the times taken for the three precipitates to form.
The quicker the precipitate is formed, the higher the rate of hydrolysis.

Ensuring a fair test

The same volume of ethanol should be used in each test tube.
The same number of moles of each haloalkane should be added to ensure the three haloalkanes are present in the same concentrations
The three haloalkanes used all have the same carbon skeleton (butane) to avoid any differences in reactivity arising from halogens being bonded to different lengths of carbon chain.
The three haloalkanes used all have their halogen atoms attached at the '1' position in the carbon chain to avoid any differences in reactivity arising from halogens being bonded at different points on the carbon chain.
All three test tubes are heated in the same water bath at the same time to ensure they are all at the same temperature.
The silver nitrate should be added to all three test tubes at the same time to ensure the three reactions start at the same time.

General equations

The haloalkanes react with the water from the silver nitrate solution to form butanol, releasing a halide ion:
$CH_3CH_2CH_2CH_2X + H_2O \rightarrow CH_3CH_2CH_2CH_2OH + H^+ + X^-$
The halide ions react with silver ions to form a silver halide precipitate:
$Ag^+ + X^- \rightarrow AgX$

Pages 68-70: Alcohols, Haloalkanes and Analysis — 3

1 a) E.g. sulfuric acid / phosphoric acid *[1 mark]*

b) Water soluble impurities can be removed using a separating funnel *[1 mark]*. Transfer the reaction mixture to the separating funnel, add water, then seal and shake the funnel and allow the mixture to settle *[1 mark]*. The reaction mixture will separate into two layers. The 1-bromobutane layer is denser and will form the lower layer *[1 mark]*. The lower layer can be run off by opening the tap at the bottom of the funnel *[1 mark]*.

c) E.g. (anhydrous) magnesium sulfate / (anhydrous) calcium chloride *[1 mark]*
The drying agent can be removed by filtration of the mixture *[1 mark]*.

d) Liquid impurities can be removed by redistillation *[1 mark]*. Heat the mixture in a round-bottomed flask connected to a Liebig condenser *[1 mark]*. A thermometer in the neck of the flask is used to monitor the temperature of the vapour *[1 mark]*. Any liquid impurities remaining will have a different boiling point to 1-bromobutane *[1 mark]*. When the boiling point of 1-bromobutane is reached, place a flask below the condenser to collect the product *[1 mark]*. When the temperature changes, a different liquid will be collected so this should be collected in a different flask *[1 mark]*.

e) Any two from: e.g. the reaction is incomplete / by-products may be produced / reagents used may be impure / some product is lost during purification / some product is lost during distillation / some of the 1-bromobutane was hydrolysed to butan-1-ol.
[2 marks — 1 mark for each valid reason.]

2 a) The M+1 peak is present due to the presence of the carbon-13 / ^{13}C isotope in the sample *[1 mark]*.

b) The m/z value of the molecular ion peak is equal to the molecular mass. / The molecular mass of compound X is 72 g mol^{-1}. *[1 mark]*

c) Ratio of C : H : O = $\frac{66.7}{12.0}$: $\frac{11.1}{1.0}$: $\frac{22.2}{16.0}$

= 5.558... : 11.1 : 1.3875

= $\frac{5.558...}{1.3875}$: $\frac{11.1}{1.3875}$: $\frac{1.3875}{1.3875}$

= 4.00... : 8 : 1
So the empirical formula of X is C_4H_8O.
[2 marks for correct empirical formula of X, otherwise 1 mark for dividing percentages of C, H and O by their relative atomic masses.]

d) How to grade your answer:
Level 0: There is no relevant information. *[No marks]*
Level 1: Interprets one or two sources of information correctly, but explanation may contain errors or omissions. *[1 to 2 marks]*
Level 2: Uses two or three of the sources of information to draw some correct conclusions about compound X but is unable to positively identify butan-2-one.
OR
Identifies compound X as butan-2-one but only partially justifies this conclusion. *[3 to 4 marks]*
Level 3: Uses relevant information from both spectra, the empirical formula and the result of the reflux experiment to deduce and fully justify that compound X is butan-2-one.
[5 to 6 marks]
Indicative chemistry content may include:
Finding the molecular formula:
The empirical formula of compound X is C_4H_8O.
The M_r of this empirical formula is
$4 \times 12.0 + 8 \times 1.0 + 16 = 72.0$.
This is equal to the molecular mass of the compound, as shown on the mass spectrum, so C_4H_8O is the molecular formula.

Identifying possible functional groups and structures:
The infrared spectrum has a sharp peak at a wavenumber of just over 1700 cm^{-1}, which suggests compound X contains a C=O/carbonyl group.
There is also a peak close to wavenumber 3000 cm^{-1}, which corresponds to the C-H groups in alkyl groups, alkenes and arenes.
There is no strong peak in the wavenumber range 3200-3600, which suggests X is not an alcohol.
There is no strong peak in the wavenumber range 1620-1680, which suggests X is not an alkene.
Compound X must therefore be one of butan-2-one ($CH_3CH_2COCH_3$), butanal ($CH_3CH_2CH_2CHO$) or 2-methylpropanal ($CH_3CH(CH_3)CHO$).
This is supported by the fragmentation pattern of the mass spectrum, however the fragmentation pattern does not provide enough information to distinguish between the three compounds.
The largest peak shown on the mass spectrum is at m/z = 43, which could be due to a CH_3CO^+ fragment from butan-2-one, a $CH_3CHCH_3^+$ fragment from 2-methylpropanal or a combination of $CH_3CH_2CH_2^+$ and CH_2CHO^+ fragments from butanal.
Identifying the compound:
The result of the experiment to reflux compound X with the oxidising agent acidified potassium dichromate(VI) shows that compound X cannot be oxidised, as an oxidation reaction would have produced a different organic compound with different mass and infrared spectra.
Aldehydes can be easily oxidised to carboxylic acids, but ketones are not easily oxidised.
Therefore compound X must be butanone.

Mixed Questions

Pages 71-73: Mixed Questions — 1

1   D *[1 mark]*
2   B *[1 mark]*
3   C *[1 mark]*

Hydrogen almost always has an oxidation number of –1 in metal hydrides.

4   C *[1 mark]*

When 2-bromopentan-3-ol is heated with aqueous sodium hydroxide, its bromine atom may be substituted for an –OH group, giving pentane-2,3-diol.

5 a) $Ca \rightarrow Ca^{2+} + 2e^-$ *[1 mark]*

  b)   +1 *[1 mark]*

Oxygen has an oxidation number of –2, and the sum of the oxidation numbers in a molecule of water is zero. Therefore, each hydrogen atom must have an oxidation number of +1.

  c)   If n is the number of moles of H_2 that occupy 100 cm³
      Then $n = (pV) \div (RT)$
          $= ((100 \times 10^3) \times (100 \times 10^{-6})) \div (8.314 \times 298)$
          $= 0.00403...$ mol
      The balanced equation for the reaction is:
      $Ca + 2H_2O \rightarrow Ca(OH)_2 + H_2$
      So 1 mole of H_2 is produced from 1 mole of Ca,
      meaning moles of Ca = 0.00403... mol
      Maximum mass of Ca = 0.00403... × 40.1 = 0.1618... g
               = 0.1618... g × 1000
               = 161.85... mg = **162 mg (3 s.f.)**

      [5 marks for correct answer, otherwise 1 mark for correctly rearranging the ideal gas equation, 1 mark for correct number of moles of H_2, 1 mark for correctly balanced reaction equation, 1 mark for mass of Ca in grams.]

  d)   E.g. some of the gas produced may have been lost from the conical flask before the gas syringe was attached. / The reaction was stopped before it could go to completion *[1 mark]*.

  e)   Barium would produce the gas in the shortest amount of time *[1 mark]*. This is because the ionisation energy is lower/the outer electron is more easily lost from barium than strontium or calcium, so barium is more reactive. / This is because barium is below calcium and strontium in Group 2, and reactivity increases going down the group *[1 mark]*.

6 a) $1s^2\ 2s^2\ 2p^6\ 3s^2\ 3p^1$ *[1 mark]*

  b)   Aluminium oxidation number: +3
      Chlorine oxidation number: –1
      [1 mark]

  c)   Aluminium has a giant metallic lattice structure and chlorine is a simple covalent substance *[1 mark]*. In aluminium there are strong electrostatic attractions between the metal ions and the sea of positive electrons *[1 mark]*. In chlorine there are weak intermolecular forces between the molecules *[1 mark]*. Aluminium has a much higher melting point because the forces that need to be overcome in aluminium are much stronger than in chlorine, so more energy is required to break the forces in aluminium *[1 mark]*.

  d)   Moles of Al = (2.00 × 1000) ÷ 27.0 = 74.074...
      From the balanced equation, 2 moles of Al reacts to form 2 moles of $AlCl_3$. So 74.074... moles of Al will react to form 74.074... moles of $AlCl_3$.
      Theoretical yield = 74.074... × 133.5 = 9888.8... g
      Percentage yield = ((7.14 × 1000) ÷ 9888.8...) × 100
               = 72.202...
               = **72.2 % (3 s.f.)**

      [3 marks for correct answer, otherwise 1 mark for moles of Al, 1 mark for theoretical yield.]

  e) $K_c = \dfrac{[Al_2Cl_6]}{[AlCl_3]^2}$ *[1 mark]*

f) i)   109.5° *[1 mark]*

  ii)
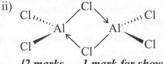

[2 marks — 1 mark for showing the correct structure, 1 mark for showing 3D bonds.]

You don't need to show the dative covalent bonds as arrows to get the marks here, but it's generally a good idea to do so.

Pages 74-77: Mixed Questions — 2

1 a) i) $CH_3CHC(CH_3)CH_2CH_3$ *[1 mark]*

    ii)

          $\begin{array}{c} H \\ H_3C \end{array} \!\!\diagdown\!\!\!\! C \!\!=\!\! C \!\!\!\! \begin{array}{c} CH_2CH_3 \\ CH_3 \end{array}$ *[1 mark]*

Make sure you remember what you're looking for with different types of isomerism. In E/Z isomerism, it's the positions of the <u>highest priority</u> groups attached to each carbon atom of the double bond that are important. In this case that's –CH₃ on the left hand carbon and –CH₂CH₃ on the right hand carbon. They're on opposite sides of the double bond so this is the E isomer. In cis-trans isomerism, it's the positions of groups that are <u>the same</u> which matter — their priorities don't come into it. So this molecule is also a cis isomer, because both of its –CH₃ groups are on the same side.

  b) i)   How to grade your answer:
      Level 0:   There is no relevant information. *[No marks]*
      Level 1:   One stage is covered well OR two stages are covered but they are incomplete and not always accurate. The answer is not in a logical order. *[1 to 2 marks]*
      Level 2:   Two stages are covered well OR all 3 stages are covered but they are incomplete and not always accurate. The answer is mostly in a logical order. *[3 to 4 marks]*
      Level 3:   All 3 stages are covered and are complete and accurate. The answer is coherent and is in a logical order. *[5 to 6 marks]*

      Indicative scientific content may include:
      <u>Shapes and polarities</u>
      Carbon dioxide contains 2 polar C=O bonds.
      The molecule is symmetrical/linear, so the charges are evenly spread across the molecule.
      This leads to the charges cancelling each other out so a molecule of carbon dioxide has no permanent dipole.
      Water contains 2 polar O–H bonds.
      The molecule is asymmetrical/bent, so the charges are unevenly spread across the molecule.
      This leads to a permanent dipole.
      <u>Intermolecular forces</u>
      Carbon dioxide is non-polar, so the only intermolecular forces acting between molecules are induced dipole-dipole/London forces.
      Water also has induced dipole-dipole/London forces acting between molecules.
      There are also permanent dipole-dipole forces between water molecules.
      These are weak electrostatic forces of attraction between the δ+ and δ– charges on neighbouring molecules.
      Water can also undergo hydrogen bonding, as it contains two O–H bonds.

Physical states

The induced dipole-dipole/London forces between carbon dioxide molecules are very weak.

So, not a lot of energy is required to break them and at room temperature carbon dioxide is a gas.

Water molecules have stronger intermolecular forces than carbon dioxide molecules.

Permanent dipole-dipole forces and hydrogen bonds require a lot more energy to break than induced dipole-dipole/London forces.

So water is a liquid at room temperature.

ii) $C_6H_{12} + 9O_2 \rightarrow 6CO_2 + 6H_2O$ *[1 mark]*

iii) $\Delta_f H\ [C_6H_{12}] = \Sigma\ \Delta_c H$ reactants $- \Sigma\ \Delta_c H$ products
$= ((6 \times -393.5) + (6 \times -285.8)) - (-4003.4)$
$= -4075.8 + 4003.4 = \mathbf{-72.4\ kJ\ mol^{-1}}$

[3 marks for correct answer, otherwise 1 mark for stating the formula and 1 mark for correctly substituting in the enthalpies of combustion.]

You'd get the mark if you drew a Hess's law diagram here, instead of stating the formula.

c) i)

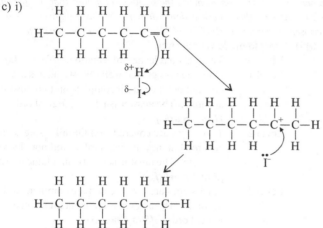

[4 marks — 1 mark for arrow from C=C to $H^{\delta+}$, 1 mark for arrow from H–I bond to $I^{\delta-}$, 1 mark for arrow from I^- to C^+, 1 mark for correct structure of product.]

ii) phosphoric acid/H_3PO_4 *[1 mark]*

iii) Hexan-2-ol contains an –OH group, so can undergo hydrogen bonding *[1 mark]*. So, more energy is required to break the intermolecular forces in hexan-2-ol than in hex-1-ene and allow it to vaporise *[1 mark]*.

2 a) i) Shape: trigonal planar *[1 mark]*
Bond angle: 120° *[1 mark]*

ii) One of the double-bond carbons has two identical groups attached to it *[1 mark]*.

b) Any one from: the double bond has a high electron density, making it likely to be attacked by electrophiles. / The π-bond has a (relatively) low bond enthalpy and so is easily broken *[1 mark]*.

c) i)

H   H   H   H   H   H
| | | | | |
—C—C—C—C—C—C—
| | | | | |
H   Cl H   Cl H   Cl   *[1 mark]*

ii) E.g. burning PVC produces toxic hydrogen chloride/HCl, which must be safely removed *[1 mark]*.

d) i) $Cl\cdot + C_2H_3Cl \rightarrow C_2H_3Cl_2\cdot$ *[1 mark]*
$C_2H_3Cl_2\cdot + C_2H_3Cl \rightarrow C_4H_6Cl_3\cdot$ *[1 mark]*

ii) E.g. the more chlorine there is in the mixture, the shorter the polymer chains will be *[1 mark]*. This is because there will be more radicals in the mixture, so termination steps are more likely to occur *[1 mark]*.

3 a) 2,2-dimethylpropan-1-ol *[1 mark]*

b) There will be a small peak at m/z = 89/M+1 *[1 mark]*. / There will be small peaks with m/z values 1 higher than those expected for the various fragment ions *[1 mark]*.

c) i)

H
|
H—C—H
|
H   H
| |
H—C——C⁺——C—H
| |
H   H   *[1 mark]*

ii) The greater the number of alkyl groups attached to the charged/central carbon in a carbocation, the more stable it is *[1 mark]*. The carbocation/fragment that is responsible for the peak at 57 m/z is a tertiary carbocation/has three alkyl groups attached, so will be relatively stable *[1 mark]*.

Data Sheet

Constants and Conversions

Molar gas volume = 24.0 dm^3 mol^{-1} at RTP (room temperature and pressure)

Avogadro constant, N_A = 6.02 × 10^{23} mol^{-1}

Specific heat capacity of water, c = 4.18 J g^{-1} K^{-1}

1 tonne = 10^6 g

Gas constant, R = 8.314 J mol^{-1} K^{-1}

Infrared Absorptions in Organic Molecules

Bond	Location	Wavenumber / cm^{-1}
C–C	alkanes alkyl chains	750 - 1100
C–X	haloalkanes (X = Cl, Br or I)	500 - 800
C–F	fluoroalkanes	1000-1350
C–O	alcohols esters carboxylic acids	1000 - 1300
C=C	alkenes	1620 - 1680
C=O	aldehydes ketones carboxylic acids esters amides acyl chlorides acid anhydrides	1630 - 1820
aromatic C=C	arenes	several peaks in range 1450-1650
C≡N	nitriles	2220 - 2260
C–H	alkyl groups alkenes arenes	2850 - 3100
O–H	carboxylic acids	2500 - 3300 (broad)
N–H	amines amides	3300 - 3500
O–H	alcohols phenols	3200-3600

The Periodic Table

Key:

Relative Atomic Mass	
Symbol	
Atomic number	Name

Example shown:
- Relative Atomic Mass → 10.8
- **B**
- 5
- Boron

(1)	(2)												(3)	(4)	(5)	(6)	(7)	(0)
1.0 **H** 1 Hydrogen																		4.0 **He** 2 Helium
6.9 **Li** 3 Lithium	9.0 **Be** 4 Beryllium												10.8 **B** 5 Boron	12.0 **C** 6 Carbon	14.0 **N** 7 Nitrogen	16.0 **O** 8 Oxygen	19.0 **F** 9 Fluorine	20.2 **Ne** 10 Neon
23.0 **Na** 11 Sodium	24.3 **Mg** 12 Magnesium												27.0 **Al** 13 Aluminium	28.1 **Si** 14 Silicon	31.0 **P** 15 Phosphorus	32.1 **S** 16 Sulfur	35.5 **Cl** 17 Chlorine	39.9 **Ar** 18 Argon
39.1 **K** 19 Potassium	40.1 **Ca** 20 Calcium	45.0 **Sc** 21 Scandium	47.9 **Ti** 22 Titanium	50.9 **V** 23 Vanadium	52.0 **Cr** 24 Chromium	54.9 **Mn** 25 Manganese	55.8 **Fe** 26 Iron	58.9 **Co** 27 Cobalt	58.7 **Ni** 28 Nickel	63.5 **Cu** 29 Copper	65.4 **Zn** 30 Zinc		69.7 **Ga** 31 Gallium	72.6 **Ge** 32 Germanium	74.9 **As** 33 Arsenic	79.0 **Se** 34 Selenium	79.9 **Br** 35 Bromine	83.8 **Kr** 36 Krypton
85.5 **Rb** 37 Rubidium	87.6 **Sr** 38 Strontium	88.9 **Y** 39 Yttrium	91.2 **Zr** 40 Zirconium	92.9 **Nb** 41 Niobium	95.9 **Mo** 42 Molybdenum	101.1 **Tc** 43 Technetium	101.1 **Ru** 44 Ruthenium	102.9 **Rh** 45 Rhodium	106.4 **Pd** 46 Palladium	107.9 **Ag** 47 Silver	112.4 **Cd** 48 Cadmium		114.8 **In** 49 Indium	118.7 **Sn** 50 Tin	121.8 **Sb** 51 Antimony	127.6 **Te** 52 Tellurium	126.9 **I** 53 Iodine	131.3 **Xe** 54 Xenon
132.9 **Cs** 55 Caesium	137.3 **Ba** 56 Barium	138.9 **La** 57 Lanthanum	178.5 **Hf** 72 Hafnium	180.9 **Ta** 73 Tantalum	183.8 **W** 74 Tungsten	186.2 **Re** 75 Rhenium	190.2 **Os** 76 Osmium	192.2 **Ir** 77 Iridium	195.1 **Pt** 78 Platinum	197.0 **Au** 79 Gold	200.6 **Hg** 80 Mercury		204.4 **Tl** 81 Thallium	207.2 **Pb** 82 Lead	209.0 **Bi** 83 Bismuth	**Po** 84 Polonium	**At** 85 Astatine	**Rn** 86 Radon
Fr 87 Francium	**Ra** 88 Radium	**Ac** 89 Actinium	**Rf** 104 Rutherfordium	**Db** 105 Dubnium	**Sg** 106 Seaborgium	**Bh** 107 Bohrium	**Hs** 108 Hassium	**Mt** 109 Meitnerium	**Ds** 110 Darmstadtium	**Rg** 111 Roentgenium	**Cn** 112 Copernicium			**Fl** 114 Flerovium		**Lv** 116 Livermorium		

The Lanthanoids

140.1 **Ce** 58 Cerium	140.9 **Pr** 59 Praseodymium	144.2 **Nd** 60 Neodymium	144.9 **Pm** 61 Promethium	150.4 **Sm** 62 Samarium	152.0 **Eu** 63 Europium	157.2 **Gd** 64 Gadolinium	158.9 **Tb** 65 Terbium	162.5 **Dy** 66 Dysprosium	164.9 **Ho** 67 Holmium	167.3 **Er** 68 Erbium	168.9 **Tm** 69 Thulium	173.0 **Yb** 70 Ytterbium	175.0 **Lu** 71 Lutetium

The Actinoids

232.0 **Th** 90 Thorium	**Pa** 91 Protactinium	238.1 **U** 92 Uranium	**Np** 93 Neptunium	**Pu** 94 Plutonium	**Am** 95 Americium	**Cm** 96 Curium	**Bk** 97 Berkelium	**Cf** 98 Californium	**Es** 99 Einsteinium	**Fm** 100 Fermium	**Md** 101 Mendelevium	**No** 102 Nobelium	**Lr** 103 Lawrencium

CRAQ51